Journey out of Nowhere

Journey out of Nowhere

Nancy Covert Smith

Word Books, Publisher □ Waco, Texas

2542

JOURNEY OUT OF NOWHERE

To my family—my reasons for getting well

To my doctor—the man who made me well

Contents

Prologue

What is mental and emotional illness?
Is the person violent?
Is it different from retardation?
Is the person crazy?
Is he permanently lost to his family and society?
How do you talk to a patient?
Can he comprehend?
Is he deaf and dumb to conversations about himself?
Should I speak slowly and loudly as to a small child?
What about treatment?
Are hospitals "snake pits"?
Do patients receive electroshock treatments as punishment?
Why do the hospitals lock the family out?
What is a psychiatrist?
Is he a shrink with his own hang-ups?
Is he a doctor who gets rich playing up rich people's neuroses?
Is he a sadist who mistreats the patients in his care?
How long is a breakdown?
How can I ward off a breakdown?
I'm thinking of killing myself!
Should I lock up my husband at home?
Will my wife get better if I'm severe with her?
He's lazy!

9

She's just being dramatic!

He's faking!

The devil's in her!

God's punishing her!

Help me!

Help her!

Help us!

People responded both by letter and in person to my first published article on mental illness. They were afraid and ignorant of the facts of mental illness. Their information had been primarily myths and horror movies. They believed nervous breakdowns happened to other people, not to them. But now they had heard the diagnosis "temporary mental illness" applied either to themselves or to members of their families, and they did not know where to turn.

The care and treatment of mental patients has advanced rapidly in recent years, but we are still afraid to take advantage of the medications, clinics, and trained workers. We are still shadowed by old wives' tales of demons and witches. We fear the unknown and unexplored, so we are reluctant to talk about mental illness or to ask questions. Because of this, mental illness is still shrouded in shame and guilt.

It is time to dissipate the myths with knowledge, love, and understanding. Because, *suddenly it can happen to you!*

For those people who came to me and for the 20,000,000 people in the United States who will at some time in their lives need psychiatric care, I have shared my experiences of a mental breakdown in this book.

Isaiah 41:6, kjv: They helped every one his neighbor: and every one said to his brother, Be of good courage!

Matthew 4:16, RSV: The people who sat in darkness
have seen a great light,
and for those who sat in the region and shadow
of death
light has dawned.

NANCY COVERT SMITH

1

Suddenly it happens to you!

In November 1967, I was thirty-two years old, a wife, and a mother to four children. I conducted two church choirs, took organ lessons that required two hours of practice a day, was president of the local Writer's Guild, was active in PTA and a dialogue group, chauffeured children to art, ballet, and piano lessons. I was busy, smiling, always willing to take on another responsibility. People shook their heads and often remarked, "I don't know how you manage."

One morning I drove to the church for my regular practicing at the organ. As I sat alone in the sanctuary, repeating the monotonous leg exercises on the foot pedals, I planned the remainder of the day. Tammy to be picked up at kindergarten, ironing, vacuuming, committee meeting, macaroni and cheese for dinner . . . Suddenly the appointments and responsibilities whirled and grew inside my head until they exploded into screams. "No! No more. I can't do any more!"

The words and screams echoed through the empty room.

The minister, working in his study, hurried to me. When he could not quiet me, he telephoned my husband.

Fifteen minutes later, in answer to the frantic call, Jim ran through the door.

To escape him I climbed over chair backs in the choir loft until I found myself cornered. My fingers clawed the walls. "Don't let him touch me!"

Gently my husband and the pastor pulled me down. They questioned me, but I covered my ears against their words. I was tired of talking. It seemed I had spent my life searching for someone who would hear me. I wanted to say, "I've told you over and over but you haven't heard me. Doesn't anyone love me enough to hear what I'm saying?"

I sank to the floor, retching.

My medical doctor was called. He prescribed a sedative. When it arrived, I gratefully gulped the medicine, hoping for unconsciousness, but I was hysterical and threw off its effects.

Intertwined with helplessness, I saw compassion and love on Jim's face and the face of the minister, and I was ashamed. I wasn't the competent person they thought I was. The mask had been torn away and I had revealed the feelings of failure, rejection, and guilt that I had lived with in secret for so many years.

I buried my face against the minister's shoulder. I didn't want to see Jim's eyes filled with bewilderment. I didn't want to see him sitting there, his hands twisting as they hung useless between his knees. I didn't want to see his throat constricting against nerves and tears. Two hours ago he had kissed me good-by at home. How could he understand?

"Don't make me go home with Jim," I pleaded. "I'm so afraid."

The pastor took me to the parsonage. His wife gave me a clean nightgown and clean sheets on the bed. Into them I put a very tired and confused body, mind, and spirit.

The following morning, the minister drove me to the hospital. We were silent during the trip. He parked the car in the lot and glanced up at the heavily screened windows at the fourth floor. "Nancy, you need help."

I nodded.

Sometime during the night the screaming and fighting had slipped out of my body and left me exhausted and empty.

He swallowed. "Do you understand where I'm taking you?"

I nodded.

"Do you want to go?"

I turned to him, tear-stained and disheveled. "I want to go."

Together we entered the emergency door. A nurse took my arm and guided me into the elevator. I turned back to my pastor for encouragement but the doors had already closed.

The nurse and I got out at the psychiatric floor. I was told to strip off my slacks and sweater and to remove my watch. I stood naked and shivering until they found a hospital gown and a faded housedress to put over it.

I removed my wedding rings.

"You can keep those," the nurse said.

I dropped them to the floor. "I don't want them. I'm not married."

I divorced myself from my family. Jim, my husband. Mark, Leanne, Craig, and Tammy—four beautiful children. I wanted them free of the guilt and burden of me. I felt I was no longer fit to be called "Mrs. Smith" or "Mother." I finally had proved what I had so long believed; I was imperfect, not worthy of love.

But while I thought I was dissolving a relationship with the simple act of removing my wedding rings, my family and a psychiatrist had already made a decision. Armed with love, understanding, compassion, and knowledge, they had begun the battle against my mental breakdown.

It was several months before I willingly joined the fight.

As I look back, I can see that I had several signals of future trouble.

As a child I sought perfection in myself and in others. I was never content with mediocrity. I wanted to excel in all that I set out to do. I never achieved the goals I set up for myself, so I sought encouragement from other people, hoping that if I heard words of praise often enough I would be convinced I was a worthwhile individual. I fell in love quickly with people, placing them on pedestals, making them personifications of ideals. In a short while they proved to be human and I cast them aside. But I always kept searching. Maybe the next person would prove worthy of my worship.

My four brothers are older, so much of my childhood I was alone. I invented a fantasy world and populated it with people who were perfect and who admired and loved me. In my world I was a beautiful woman sitting under a tree, my flowered dress spread around me. Below me was a valley, sunshiny and peaceful. Whenever the world of reality became boring or antagonistic toward me I escaped to a corner of the pasture field, my playhouse, or my bedroom. There I rocked to and fro and lived in my make-believe world.

As I grew older, I spent less time in my land of princes and

flower gardens. I turned to activity. By the time I was eleven I
was playing the piano for church services. I attended meetings with
my mother because I could answer all of the questions asked in
the study book. I went home happy when the women remarked
to my mother, "You must be very proud of her." My self-image
was so bad I couldn't believe anyone could love me for myself,
but only for what I could do.

In high school I became involved accompanying the choirs and
glee clubs, playing in the band and orchestra. I spoke in the Prince
of Peace contests and the individual speech events. I was in the
plays and operettas. I enjoyed being in front of a group, performing.
I needed the praise and acceptance of the crowd. If enough people
congratulated me, maybe I would eventually believe I really was
a worthwhile person.

That assurance didn't come. I needed more and more attention
to be satisfied. I gave twenty piano lessons a week and was president
of our youth group for four years. There wasn't enough time in
the week to compete in all the contests I needed to feed my growing
addiction.

The ending of school was a relief. I reached graduation exhausted.

The years following I lived in a mild depression. I had run so
hard during the mania that I was content to rest. My brief secretarial
job brought me new friends and new interests. My marriage to Jim
brought fulfillment and the excitement of moving to California and
my first apartment. Before I tired of being a housekeeper, Mark
arrived and I was caught up in the privilege of caring for a baby.

Shortly after we moved back to Ohio, Leanne joined Mark, and
I was busy changing diapers for two. By the time we had moved
into the first home we owned, Craig and Tammy had been added
to the family and I had grown fat and, on the surface, content.
I cleaned, cooked, sewed, and canned the vegetables from the garden.
While I nursed Tammy I read novels. We played cards with my
parents at least once a week, and the evenings Jim worked late,
I took the children to the root beer stand and then to the drive-in
theater. It wasn't a very stimulating routine. At the age of twenty-
seven I looked older than I do now.

My husband changed jobs and we moved again, this time to Dayton.
It was here that I felt the first feelings of mania returning. There

was no perfection possible in rearranging and removing dirt. I felt trapped by housework and taken for granted by my family.

My search for praise began again. I became a den mother for twelve Cub Scouts, determined that all of my scouts would earn their Wolf badges. I joined the choir, took a night course in writing with the goal of writing the best story in the class. I became Primary superintendent at the church; the children would learn more than they ever had before. Two hours a day I wrote. Look at me! See my accomplishments!

I did not lose weight. I still felt dowdy and unattractive. I bought my clothes at a second-hand store because I felt it was useless to waste money on pretty clothes that did not look pretty on me. But at that time I wasn't analyzing any of my problems. I just rushed from one project to the next, hoping for instant satisfaction.

In 1964 I had my first publication. This, I decided, was the answer. If a hundred people at church didn't realize I was talented, then certainly thousands of people reading my material would be sufficient gratification.

Jim took a new job in Canton and left almost immediately for the northeast part of Ohio. It was six months before we could buy our present home and the children and I could join him. We moved in on July 4. By September I had agreed to direct the adult choir. By Christmas time I had taken over the children's choir. The move had not slowed me down. If anything, faced with the task of making friends in another new place, I worked even harder for acceptance.

By May of 1967 I knew I was in serious trouble. Afraid to be alone, I avoided solitude whenever possible. I had lost thirty pounds. I thought then it was because finally I had the will power to stay on a diet. I know now I would have lost weight regardless. My appetite was gone.

Routine chores made me impatient. I avoided work by hiding it in closets. My flower garden grew up to weeds. I was always tired but I couldn't rest. My eyes stared wide, far into the night. I lay with my fists clenched as thoughts raced over themselves in my mind. And blanketing it all was the smothering emptiness of loneliness.

The next month I was preparing for Choir Sunday. The last Sunday before summer recess was devoted to an hour's worship in song.

I spent several hours at the church going through the files of music, picking out favorites and mixing difficult anthems with easier folk hymns for variety. This would be my best program of the year! The pastor stopped in often while I was working, or I visited his study before I left for the day. I was my usual laughing self. He talked to me as a friend. I didn't hint that I had a serious thought, though inside I was struggling for the courage to ask for help.

One day he walked with me to the car. Before I drove away I said, "Someone has to love Nancy Smith." I was ashamed that my voice broke. I glanced into the rear-view mirror as I drove away and saw that he watched my car out of sight.

He recognized that plea for help. Slowly I confided in him. By July I was revealing feelings I had never before confessed. He suggested I seek professional help, but I was stubborn. I could handle this myself!

He repeatedly asked me to talk to Jim, but I was firm. I had tried one night, but Jim had fallen asleep during the one-sided conversation. I was definite about secrecy. I made the minister promise he would not tell anyone that I was troubled. How could I, who expected perfection from others, admit that I was running headlong toward failure?

All during this time, still successfully wearing the smiling mask, I forced the pastor to share the burden without allowing him any freedom to deal with it.

The last week in August, friends of the church paid my tuition to a music camp in New York State. The pastor thought it might be good for me to get away for a week. I thought, too, that it would give me a chance to sort out my fears and, hopefully, to cope with them. But completely on my own, surrounded by strangers, I was soon aware of how nervous I was. The curriculum proved to be far beyond my little training. I was enrolled with professors holding doctor's degrees in music. This competition was beyond me. Each day I lived in fear that someone would ask me a question and discover how inferior I was. When one of the teachers corrected my conducting pattern, I attacked him in front of several other students. My behavior was erratic, my mood unpredictable. I wasn't able to make a friend.

Alone in my tiny room at night, I cried until three and four in the morning. I counted the days until I could get home and tell the minister how inferior and lonely I felt. He would reassure me I was talented. I knew he would.

How defeated he was as I stood before him, weeping, the day I returned home. At the same time I pleaded with him to perform a miracle, I tied his hands so he couldn't consult anyone who could help me.

By now I was vomiting every morning as soon as I awoke, and I had diarrhea. The medical doctor, unaware of any emotional problems, presumed the trouble was ulcers and put me on a diet of unflavored gelatin and skim milk. The muscles in my back tightened until pain numbed both arms. Our family life was laced with quarrels and long silences. I put the blame on Jim, on circumstances, on short finances, on too much housework, on everything but the real basis for the conflict—my unreasonable goal of perfection in everything.

Almost immediately after choir convened in the fall, I began working on the Christmas program. This year it would involve *three* choirs, piano, and organ—one hour of music without a spoken word.

Besides this, in the spring the organist was leaving and I wanted his job. I began organ lessons. He was a good organist, so I would have to work hard to be better.

I planned a Hallowe'en party for twelve people.

I started sewing clothes for the two girls.

Thank God He has given us bodies that will act when we reach the limit of endurance but are too foolish to recognize and admit physical and mental exhaustion! When I would not stop, my mind protected itself by breaking from reality. Suddenly—after thirty years—it happened to me!

The small task of macaroni and cheese was the final responsibility that my mind would not accept.

Those first screams at the church crumpled my mask. I was through pretending—to myself, to my family, to the public. I was tired of trying to please them, tired of hiding my confusion and feelings of inadequacy. My admission, in the hospital parking lot, that I wanted to go was finally an honest one. But ahead of me lay a long, hard journey.

My first reaction to the hospital was a tumult of questions. Looking at the other patients, I wondered, "How did I reach the point of confinement with these people?" Surely I had nothing in common with derelicts drying out, vulgar-mouthed women, attempted suicides. I had no connection with a room that had straps on the bed. Why look at me, I could think. I knew where I was. But how had I gotten here? I wasn't crazy. "Oh, God, I am not crazy!"

All patients had to be x-rayed on admittance. An orderly came for me, walked me through the ward, and unlocked the door. Together we went down to the first floor. I pulled at the ill-fitting housedress and tried to smoothe my hair. I didn't want to be seen this way. Members of the hospital staff openly stared at me. I soon understood why. They recognized the orderly. They knew he worked the psychiatric floor. They were curious to see what I might do. As I followed him through the halls, I felt like a freak at a side show, or a monkey on a leash.

In the waiting room for x-ray, I was told to sit down until it was my turn. The orderly stood at the door talking to a nurse. He didn't have to watch me; his body blocked the only exit. I leafed through a magazine. The other people in the waiting room stopped reading and watched me. Was I expected to entertain? Didn't they know that I knew they were staring at me? Perhaps I wasn't entitled to good manners. Not if I was kept under lock and key.

When my turn finally came, the nurse seemed especially rough. Had I always received such abrupt treatment in the hospital? My other visits had been the births of the children. Was the attitude of the staff more considerate of a new mother than a mental patient? Or did I feel persecuted because I was expecting unkindness, and when we look for unkindness we never have trouble finding it?

At last the examinations were complete and we walked back to the elevator. The orderly rang. As we were waiting, the outside door opened and Jim walked in. I saw him before he saw me. I pressed myself against the wall and turned my head, hoping he wouldn't recognize me.

I heard the whisper of the elevator and was grateful for the opening doors. The orderly took my arm and guided me inside. When I turned around, I glimpsed Jim standing alone and dejected, staring at me and the closing doors.

The image stayed with me as I returned to my room.

I had been definite about not seeing my husband, so the nurse came to inform me about what I already knew. "Your husband is outside. If you don't want to see him, it's quite all right. I'll tell him to leave." She added with a kind sternness, "But remember, Nancy, this is the only time you can see him. After today it will be eight days before he is allowed to return."

My mind was muddled. I wanted to save Jim this nightmare. I didn't want to shame my family. But I needed him. I wasn't strong enough to say no. Fearfully I said, "I'll see him."

I sat on the edge of the bed, waiting. What would I say? I'm sorry? How could an apology compensate for the terrible thing I was doing to him? How could I bear to look at him? How could I bear to have him look at me? I twisted my hands and wished I had told the nurse to send him away.

Then I heard the nurse say, "Your wife's in there."

Jim answered, "Thank you."

I heard his footsteps. He has a way of shuffling his feet when he's nervous. The little cough I recognized as his habit when he is self-conscious.

I didn't look up.

After a silence he said, "I bought you these."

He placed several boxes beside me on the bed. I noticed the labels were from a store too expensive for me to patronize.

"Open them."

I lifted the lid on the first box. It held a white nightgown, embroidered with pink roses. The next one contained a pale blue robe, the third a gown and robe in deep rose encrusted in lace, the last a pair of soft pink slippers.

I thought, For me? Why should I put these pretty things on me?

Finally I made myself look up at Jim. His face was contorted. Tears began to fall. He dropped to his knees, buried his face in my lap, and sobbed, "What have I done to you?"

It had not occurred to me that he would be feeling responsible! Over his head I stared at my reflection in the mirror. My hair hung in disheveled strings. It hadn't been combed that morning. My face was swollen from crying, dark circles lay on my cheeks. Only yesterday I had been at home getting the children ready for school. How

could all this have happened in a few short hours? I knew that
I wasn't crazy or violent, that I was not likely to require permanent
commitment. But I also knew that I needed to be in this place.
I knew what I had in common with the other people on this floor.
All of us, in our own way, were incapable of living!

I cradled Jim's head. "You've done nothing to me."

Briefly a small spark within me vowed that reflection, "My family
deserves better than me. I will get well!"

I lay back on the bed, my knees drawn up, my back to Jim
and the door. I was so tired. Sometime I would try. Yes—but not
now.

I stopped fighting.

②

What about the family?

To those of us involved in temporary mental illness, it seems to be a lonely and uncharted journey, yet according to the National Association for Mental Health, Inc., twenty million persons, or one in ten, in the United States, will at some time in their lives have some form of mental or emotional illness that would benefit from professional help. We cannot be alone if half of our hospital beds are occupied by the mentally ill, and we are increasing that number at the rate of two hundred and fifty thousand a year. It is time that we acknowledge the diagnosis "mental illness" and discuss practically its symptoms and recovery. Fear and shame have too long been the enemies of mental health. We must support and promote its allies—understanding and knowledge—because seven out of ten patients admitted to hospitals can leave partially or totally recovered when given prompt and proper treatment.

The mounting numbers of mentally ill are too often attributed to "the fast pace we live." After experiencing a breakdown and working closely with numerous people fighting mental and emotional problems I would rather believe the statistical rise indicates that we, as a nation, are finally recognizing the need and usefulness of psychiatric care, and that we are seeking help rather than shutting our disturbed loved ones in an upstairs bedroom and learning to "live with it."

There are two forms of mental illness—organic and functional.

23

Organic mental illnesses result from defects that occur in the brain before birth or when injury or illness cause damage to the brain. Functional mental illnesses involve no apparent change in the brain, yet the mind does not work properly. Most mental illness is functional and it is that form which is the subject of this book.

Functional mental illness has been described as a neurosis out of control. There are several types of neuroses—anxiety, conversion, hypochondria, obsession, compulsion, phobias and depression. We all have a touch of the neurotic; there are chronic lint-pickers, picture-straighteners, etc. But when a person suffers from unfounded fear, uncontrolled drives, smothering depression, he is no longer in control. He is being ruled by his neurosis.

A major emotional illness may be diagnosed as a psychosis—paranoia, schizophrenia, manic depression. The line between neurotic and psychotic is fine, and often even doctors disagree on the division.

Though the causes of temporary mental illness differ, it is important to note that many of the *symptoms* are similar and the *progress to recovery* is similar. This is why sharing of experience between families of patients and between patients themselves is beneficial.

My record reads "depressive." My depressive reactions included "blue" feelings, lack of decision, loss of appetite and feelings of being inadequate to face life. During the mania I talked excessively and moved about a great deal. I seemed to be happy, but was usually sad on the inside.

Because, as is characteristic of most mental patients, I was clever at masking my true feelings, my breakdown was an immediate shock to my family. Without preparation, they were thrown into a frightening and strange situation. Unlike the situation with many physical ailments, there was no advance notice given to the family. The doctor did not sit down and describe the condition and suggest treatment. The breakdown occurred seemingly in an instant. The psychiatrist who was called in was unknown to my family and to me. He had no choice but to hospitalize me and begin with emergency measures.

But what about my family? What would happen to them? What would life be like for them over the two or more years of my recovery?

A year and a half after my breakdown, *McCall's* magazine published the first mental illness article I wrote. From the response I received, I realized people react in various ways to a breakdown.

Some refuse to accept the diagnosis, some hide the patient, some abandon the patient. I concluded that the immediate reaction of the majority of people was to hide the problem rather than face it. On the surface that seems like the easiest solution. "We'll make up a story to tell the children." "We won't tell the neighbors." Soon the situation is a tangled web of lies. By the time the patient has returned home the circumstances have become so complicated that he literally *does* have to be hidden away for a long period of time. With this unhealthy beginning it is quite obvious that the patient's recovery will be hampered, if not prohibited.

Jim and I did not have time to talk about what we would do. It was just fortunate that we both felt the same way about mental illness. We both accepted the diagnosis. We both called my illness a "breakdown." Though it is purely a laymen's term, it explains the type of sickness without having to go into medical terms. Beginning on the day of my admittance, we talked without apology or shame about my breakdown, and Jim told people, when they asked, that I was receiving help in the psychiatric ward. We have never regretted our decision.

As soon as I was receiving care in the hospital and my medication had been prescribed, the psychiatrist turned his attention to Jim. In the first few days following such an explosive event it is important to keep any other member of the family from following the patient into the hospital.

Until I had had the opportunity to rest and become somewhat calm, there was little the doctor could do to help me. He concentrated on Jim and his problems. Jim had to continue with his work and assume the crushing responsibilities of four children, a sick wife, and skyrocketing expenses on top of constant worry. He could not afford to be ill himself. To help him cope, the doctor prescribed a medicine to relax him and another to help him sleep.

In helping Jim adjust to the situation, several hours were spent getting the history of the family and my own personal history. The doctor let Jim "get off his chest" his explosions of feelings. He explored more fully Jim's reaction "What did I do to put Nancy in the hospital?" Jim needed assurance that the guilt was not all on his shoulders.

Until he had had time to accept what was happening, he needed an outlet for his emotions and he needed to rely on someone. The doctor provided this sounding board and supplied this strength.

That first day, after school, the children had to be told. Mark was twelve, Leanne eleven, Craig seven, Tammy five. How much could they understand? How frightened were they by the mysterious absence of their mother? How much of Jim's desolation and confusion did they sense?

People were ready with advice. They favored pretense. Tell them, "Mommy's gone away for a rest." Some counseled, "The truth will leave them open to ridicule from other children." Or, "They're too young, spare them."

But, looking into their eyes, Jim couldn't lie. Anything they imagined, in their beds at night, after all the lights were out, would be more frightening than the facts.

He explained, "Mommy is ill. She has had a nervous breakdown. Her mind is sick and the doctor is working to make her well. She is in the hospital and the nurses are taking care of her so she can rest. As soon as she is able, she will be back home with us."

The next morning at school, Tammy, missing the affection of a mother, climbed upon her teacher's lap. She carefully explained to Mrs. Bowen where Mommy had gone. It was then easy for the teacher to understand the loneliness of a little girl. She began saving fifteen minutes each morning before classes to give affection to a little girl who needed a substitute mommy.

This was just the beginning of the children's showing special understanding and love. They also proved the adults wrong. No child ever chanted, "Your mother's crazy." Armed with the truth and a matter-of-fact explanation, the children and their peers discussed and accepted what adults were still reluctant to put into words.

Jim realized he had to accept emergency help. He was dazed and needed a period of adjustment. Everyday routine had to be maintained, but he could not immediately cope with all of the unaccustomed demands. Also, friends and neighbors, stunned by the news, needed a tangible outlet for their concern.

The response from the church was immediate. The first to arrive was Ginny, a friendly, grandmotherly woman who had recently been widowed. She volunteered to care for the children. Each day at noon, she picked up Tammy from kindergarten and stayed until

Jim came home after evening visiting hours at the hospital. Jim was able to depend on her during my hospitalization. Ronalee and Arlene took turns picking up the laundry and returning it clean and ironed. They continued this several weeks even after I was home. Five women came on Fridays to clean the house. Every meal for over six weeks was brought in hot and ready for the table.

We needed this attention. We could not have afforded to pay for the services these people donated and we could not have adjusted so quickly to the circumstances without this supporting love—another reason, we found, why it was important to realistically admit to and face a breakdown. It is too enormous a problem to surmount alone.

When people say to me now, "My neighbor is having problems, but I don't know what I can do," I tell them, "If you can bake a pie or iron a shirt, you can do something very important."

How do you say thank you to so many people? We eventually decided to place a bouquet of pink roses on the church altar. Pink roses—the floral symbol of friendship.

As the days stretched into weeks, Jim knew he had to make long-range plans. We would not be able to depend on others through my entire recovery. The doctor had told Jim when I did come home I would not be able to resume running the house. I would be unable to drive a car for a period of time. Also I would have to see the doctor three times a week.

When we better understood my condition we telephoned our parents and told them. My mother came to help as soon as I was discharged. She stayed for awhile, but how long I do not know because my mind then was not retaining information.

Jim learned to shop and to sort clothes for the laundromat. Leanne began cooking. The children got themselves ready for school. They proved to be competent and self-sufficient beyond their years when they realized the necessity of helping.

Jim sat for hours in the doctor's waiting room reading *Esquire* and *The New Yorker*, while he tried not to think of the work piling up on his desk at the office or that this was also the day for Leanne's piano lesson. He was trying to allow the children to continue their interests. We did not want them to have to give up too much.

Jim sat down and figured exactly how much of the expenses would be covered by insurance. We were fortunate. Our policy covered psychiatric care in the hospital and also a portion of each visit to the psychiatrist. He arranged with the doctor to pay a portion of our bill on a regular basis.

Next came a new schedule of family living. This was *our* problem, something we as a family had to cope with. Jim gave up all of his extra activities. He had no time for committee meetings and bowling. Each member of the family had specific jobs. It was probably good that I was withdrawn. I have an idea the corners of the house piled up with dust and that the clutter was merely pushed out of sight. But what was important, we found by not sitting down feeling sorry for ourselves we could manage!

What we were not prepared for was the people who did not believe I was sick, the people who rejected the diagnosis "mental illness." I came to hate the words, "There's nothing wrong with you. You're just fine." Smothered by depression, I wanted to shake the people who spoke them. I wanted to know, "Why won't you let me be sick?"

People recovering from a gall bladder operation, a broken leg, a heart attack, are given the right to convalesce. We do not argue with them that their ailments are imaginary. Just because my scar did not show did not mean I had no actual complaint. It was not a figment of my imagination. I recently heard a man ask a psychiatrist, "Why do depressive people keep pretending they are too tired to work? Why don't they admit they are lazy?"

The doctor answered, "Because they are not lazy. They are too tired to work."

Constantly I had to contend with people's accusations that I was "faking" my illness.

As we were to come to understand in the following months of my recovery, when there is a misunderstanding or a question between society and the patient, it is the patient and his family who make the adjustment. It was we who had to be understanding. The doctor explained it this way. "Many people refuse to accept the diagnosis because, if they do, they may have to ask themselves what part they played in the breakdown. Rather than honestly confronting that question, they block it from their minds by refusing to admit that there is a problem."

We had to learn to hide our antagonism and to smile when people relieved their consciences by resorting to polite clichés. Arguments and explanations do no good against a closed mind. The people who understood responded when there was a need. Those who offered empty phrases of cheer and left with the words, "Call me if you need anything," we dismissed.

Words we longed to hear were, "I understand—I've been there." We would have welcomed knowing another family who had accomplished the recovery to productive living. But it wasn't until a year later that I met my first ex-patient. Not long after, I also received a letter from an editor who had experienced a breakdown. The reassurances of these two people gave us something tangible to cling to when we became discouraged. If only more people would remember their own experience and share with others what they had learned, the way would not be so frightening.

Eventually people lost interest altogether. People stopped calling on the telephone and stopped coming to visit. It seemed the place we held in the community and in the church was gone. It was as though we had moved or even died. People busy with their own problems and harried schedules forgot us. We tried not to be too upset. We were not unique. After all, isn't this true for people with terminal illness, bedfast people, the handicapped, the aged? We all are too busy to remember the loneliness and heartache of others.

We received one party invitation after my discharge. We went. I sat by the fireplace and listened to the conversation. The noise disturbed me and I did not talk, but I liked watching the games. I suppose it was difficult for the others to be gay when I was sitting motionless and quiet. But I appreciated the companionship of people. It was good to see Jim laugh again. But there was never another invitation.

Jim and I had done much entertaining. We had often had several families in. While the adults talked or played games in the living room, the children roller-skated in the basement or played hide-and-seek outside. In the summer we had spur-of-the-moment picnics. Everyone brought a contribution and their own hot dogs and hamburgers. Now this had stopped. The children, small enough to depend on us entirely for entertainment, had no social life. People did not know how to react to me, so they excluded the entire family. I had robbed my family of fitting comfortably into a group.

After two years we knew that the majority of our old friends were never going to consider me "normal." The wall of embarrassment and hesitation did not decrease. Our close friends now are people we have met since 1967. These people, though they know my history, are relaxed and treat me as a competent individual. It was easier to cultivate new friends than it was to try to prove to people who had known me before that I could once again be a responsible person. It is a sad fact that people who are unable to accept mental illness as an illness also cannot accept the fact that it is curable. People were not consistent. They argued that my sickness was imaginary, but they treated me as though I would never be responsible again.

Problems outside the family were enough to try the patience of Jim and the children, but in addition there was the disharmony within the family. The family tried to remember that my welfare came before their own feelings. They continually reminded themselves that they were living with an irrational person. Many times they wanted to scold, "Use your head. Make sense."

But this is what I could not do. This was my sickness, the inability to be logical.

Patience had to be meted out in great quantities. There were rules to be remembered:

1. Don't answer her shouted accusations.
2. Don't argue with what she says.
3. Suggest a job to busy her, but be prepared to do it without reprimand when she doesn't respond.
4. Stop expecting quick results. Instead expect long days and weeks when there seems to be no progress at all.

But they were human. How do you live two years without a selfish thought? How do you keep from striking back in anger? How do you cope with wanting to stomp out of the house, filled with self-pity, vowing never to come back?

As time dragged by, we found that the best way to clear the air was with a few violent explosive words, followed by an hour alone. Long periods of martyred silence did more to hold me in depression than one explosion of temper. And it was a welcome relief of tension for Jim. The only requirement for this method: Don't feel guilty! Forgive yourself and return to the patient with love and a renewed spirit.

Leanne showed the most strength with this problem. She is the least demonstrative of the children, so perhaps it came more natural to her to cope calmly with my gamut of uncontrolled emotions. I remember clinging to her one Sunday afternoon and repeating, "I'm crazy. I don't want to be crazy, but I am crazy!"

She did not contradict me. She offered no flippant promises of instant recovery. She silently held me in her arms.

Would life ever be anything for any of us but this hell?

Craig tiptoed down the stairs late one night and crawled into Jim's lap for comfort. Leaning against his daddy's chest, he whispered, "How much longer until Mommy is well?"

Alone, in the silence of late night, Jim searched for the words to reassure a seven-year-old boy and also still the question in his own adult mind, "How long? How long?" He had no positive words to give to Craig, but as he felt the trust of Craig's hand in his, he knew the answer lay there. As long as we could turn to each other for a clasped hand or a silent embrace, we would find the strength to keep trying.

3

Behind locked doors

I sympathize with the member of the family chosen to accompany the patient to the hospital. This is only one of the difficult responsibilities of the next months or years, but it is one of the first steps, on an unknown journey and so especially frightening.

The elevator is locked, then unlocked and locked at each floor as it climbs to the psychiatric ward. The door of the ward is unlocked by an orderly. They walk through and it thuds shut, locked behind them. In the rooms are locked closet doors, locked bureau drawers. Windows have heavy screens locked into place.

Papers are pushed forward. "Sign these." With a pen clutched in his hand, he feels the thousands of questions pressing in on his brain, but one of them battles to the front and explodes. "How? My God, how can I do this to someone I love?"

The starched uniform says again, "Sign these." The pen moves. A part of the family has been committed. The patient is led away. The orderly unlocks the door for the other person, who hurries out, hoping to escape the sound of the key grating in the lock. On the street, he looks up. It is easy to pick out the psychiatric floor by the heavy screens. He looks about him. He is outside. Those people are locked inside. Each breath of clean, fresh air is a stab of punishment and guilt.

For awhile the locked side of that door was my home. And it is a home. Here is a unique society inhabited by people with problems—people who no longer hide behind masks, but who are searching

32

for answers to their problems. Here is a haven where responsibilities and decisions have been taken away and will only be returned in small doses as the patient is able to cope with them.

After I was admitted, I was asked to undress and put on a hospital gown. Over this they put a faded housedress. Dressed this way, I was embarrassed to take the "tour" of the ward, but the nurses refused to pamper my vanity. They took my arm and led me out into the hall.

My room was by the nurses' station. Straight ahead were other bedrooms. Each room was arranged to accommodate two women and contained two beds, two bureaus, and two comfortable chairs. Down the other hall was a women's ward and a men's ward, the television and reading room, the game room, the shower, and a dining room that doubled as a meeting place.

I was aware of being watched by the other thirty-five patients. I envied them their experience. They had already gone through all of the "firsts." They belonged. I was the new one, the strange one.

The tour ended at the dining room at lunch time. I was seated at a table with three other people. A tray was put in front of me. The nurses left. I looked at the staple hospital food and wondered how I could unfold my napkin, pick up a fork, and force myself to eat.

Then across from me a man said, "Anybody here doesn't want his milk? I'll trade my pineapple juice."

A woman picked up her carton of milk and the trade was made. The buzz of conversation picked up. Tapioca was traded for pickled beets. Snatches of sentences stood out. "I had first in line for bath this morning."

"You on the orange capsule?"

"Treatment this morning?"

These people were communicating, responding to one another. I expected them to be violent, sullen, odd. I had thought I would be the only one coherent. My surprise must have shown, because the woman to my left said, "You're new, aren't you? After lunch I'll introduce you around."

I tried to return her smile. Maybe I could eat something after all.

I became acquainted that afternoon with hospital schedule and the people. As I met the people I was most grateful that no one asked, "Why are you here?" I soon learned this is a personal thing and everyone respects everyone else's privacy. We admitted to and discussed our problems only when we were ready.

The schedule was simple. Lights came on at 7:00 A.M. Patients were prepared for a cardiograph, blood test, vitamin shot, the doctor's visit, or an electroshock treatment. If we hadn't been scheduled for anything, we bragged about it at breakfast.

After breakfast, a bell rang and we formed a line for pills. By 9:00 A.M. we had reassembled in the dining room, this time with clean clothes, towel, soap, shampoo, hair rollers—whatever it took to make us fresh for a new day. There were thirty-five patients and only one shower, so the line moved slowly. No one complained—much—because no one was short of time.

I found that fashion was important. The women were eager to see the changes of gowns and robes. And for a mother who had always worn plain nightgowns, I appreciated slipping into my rose colored set. (The men seemed content with their traditional striped pajamas and plaid flannel robes.) We took turns fixing each other's hair and sitting under the dryer. We asked the nurses for our make-up and experimented with each other's perfumes and nail polishes. The staff encouraged us to be clean and neat for visiting hours, even if we weren't expecting a visitor.

We were also encouraged to circulate. During the day we could read, listen to records, play games, put together puzzles, watch TV, play cards, play the piano, or knit. If we had all been well, it would have sounded like the planned program of summer camp. But we weren't well, so it was difficult to concentrate on reading the wrinkled and torn back issues of magazines. Puzzles lacked pieces or the pieces resisted our clumsy fingers and were brushed to the floor to be picked up by a nurse's aide. The record player was loud and monotonous because we had only a few records, and arguments resulted as to whether the phonograph would be turned off or turned up. Players labored over shuffling cards. Stitches continually slipped off knitting needles and required concentration to be picked up.

Everyone welcomed the relief of lunch. Though the starchy meals weren't tempting, we ate them and gained weight. (I gained fifteen pounds during my stay.)

After lunch was the pill line again and then visiting hours! The time was to come when I would wait hopefully each time for the door to open. As patients responded to treatment and were able to appreciate company, visitors (the immediate family only) shortened the long afternoon. The dining room filled with people. The left-over patients went to the end of the hall and talked to each other, not wanting to interfere with those who had company.

Supper was served early. As darkness crept in, we grew restless. We walked the halls, slowed down by medication and depression, yet not able to relax or sit quietly for very long. Some patients were given jobs at the nurses' station. It seemed like a long time until evening visiting hours. But it was routine and soon familiar, a very important thing because the patients relied on this sameness. And I, as they, welcomed this security.

The people were more interesting than the schedule. My psychiatrist attributes 50 percent of the healing process to the society of the psychiatric ward. When I questioned another doctor as to the legitimacy of this statement, he said he would even say 60 percent. Humor, love, compassion, tears, anger, patience—they were all here. Very quickly these weren't just people, but individuals, separate personalities.

Brenda* came from Georgia. She had long black hair and wiggled her hips when she walked. They had taken away her dentures and she regularly cursed the attendants for making her look old.

Sally, my roommate, was separated from her third husband, with her regular problem, another man.

Jerry, who was forty-nine, looked much older. His hair was white and his whiskers grizzled. He had gone on a two-week drunk and ended up in our ward. He had been through "drying out" several times before.

Carrie, black and rumpled, was just old. Her wants were small—cigarettes, whiskey, and a chew. Though she asked each of us, every day, for all three, none of us could help her. She compensated by slipping into our rooms and eating whole boxes of candy. She was our pet, our elderly grandma, in her second childhood.

---

*The names of the patients have all been changed.

Pauline, a young Negro with a protruding stomach, told us the bulge was a baby, but she wasn't pregnant.

Dori slashed her wrists one evening and was admitted. She was a Filipino and we struggled to understand her limited English.

The baby of the ward, Kim, was fourteen, a habitual runaway. She had broken her glasses and used the slivers of glass to tear at her flesh.

Bill, twenty-one years old, had attempted suicide. He was pulled from his car after he had crashed head-on into a concrete abutment.

Josh, tall and lanky, was a Texan on the move. He had been a chef and he gave us recipes to try when we got home. (Somehow the broiled bananas spread with peanut butter and wrapped in bacon didn't turn out to be very tasty!)

Al broke down at work and was led away from his job to come here where someone continued to lead him.

Long-haired Dave was guilt-ridden because he believed he had caused the death of his buddy in Vietnam.

These people became my best friends in the hospital.

Humor played an important part in our lives. We knew the difference, though, between ridicule and laughing at ourselves. How could any of us point a finger at another individual when our residence here confirmed the fact that we also had a problem? But many difficult moments were conquered because of our ability to laugh.

After lunch we congregated in the TV room to have our temperatures and blood pressures taken, and to report on the constant question, "Did your bowels move since yesterday?" When the nurse turned her back, thermometers were laid on radiators, or held against ice cubes. "The question" was answered with everything except yes or no. When finally pinned down to an embarrassed yes, the victim received an ovation from the group. Needless to say, the nurses drew straws to see who was stuck with this job.

Afternoons the knitters met at the window. We weren't allowed to have a comb or glass container in our possession at any time, but a dozen women could congregate, unchaperoned, with 14-inch steel knitting needles—one of the hospital rules we never figured out. In the time I was hospitalized, I didn't knit across even one row. Because of the sedation I had no natural rhythm. Each stitch was accomplished by holding the left needle between my knees. With my left hand I pushed the right needle through the stitch. My right hand maneuvered the yarn around the right needle and held it tight. Slowly I drew the right needle out but dropped the stitch. With a sigh I started over. Luckily I was on a knit row; I'm sure I couldn't have coped with purling.

Two nurse's aides who enjoyed playing euchre came on duty with a deck of cards in their pockets. As soon as they had finished their work, they looked for partners. Watching a card game was like seeing a slow-motion film. When a patient shuffled, the result was cards on the floor, the dealer's lap, and perhaps a half dozen on the table. Dealing was concentrated labor. Five cards dealt was an accomplishment. The nurse's aides gossiped and waited patiently. None of the staff ever stepped in to do anything for a patient that he was capable of doing for himself. How often they must have gritted their teeth and clenched their fists to keep from interfering and saying, "Let me do it and get it done." They knew no matter how slowly we moved or how much effort it was for us to express ourselves, it was important for us to do so.

Love and compassion were personified many times. Daily charts were kept, and if you didn't eat you were on record as "patient refusing food." Since the staff was too busy to care for each person individually, usually the elderly patients stared into their trays, their hands limp in their laps. Dave, the boy with the Jesus-cut, always sat at a table with the senile women. Wolfing his food, as teen-age boys do, he finished eating in a few minutes. He then took a spoonful of food, held it to a lady's lips and with his free hand gently moved the lower jaw open. Talking quietly all the while, he encouraged her to chew the food. When it was swallowed, he patted her cheek and praised her. The reward for his hour of effort and patience was a tiny, tired smile, a few extra bites for himself, and the guilt over the death of his buddy pushed a little farther back in his mind.

Kim, the runaway, was a bright girl who talked and laughed a lot. One night a young Negro boy was wheeled in and put into the one private room. By breakfast time the next morning we all knew that Johnny had swallowed acid and that his throat, tongue, and esophagus were burned and blistered. His records stated "no talking." On his bed lay a pad of paper and a pencil, but he refused to pick them up. He turned his head away from the door. We were concerned but we were at a loss to know how to reach him.

Kim wasn't stopped that easily. She carried in a chair, sat by his bed, and talked. Mornings, afternoons, evenings, she talked. He stayed turned toward the wall. She carried in magazines and read aloud. She worked crossword puzzles out loud. She gossiped about everyone in the ward and told him jokes about the nurses.

Finally, one day, Johnny turned over in bed. For a long time he stared at Kim. Then he reached for his pad and pencil. Across it he scrawled, "Want to put together a jigsaw puzzle with me?"

Kim jumped up from the chair and ran down the hall shouting into every room, "Johnny talked. He talked to me on his paper!"

Johnny watched her go, a grin across his face. We all wondered if he really wanted to put together a puzzle or if he decided this was the only way he was going to stop Kim's incessant talking.

I played the piano. Probably badly at that time, if my knitting was an example of my coordination. But, regardless, the patients liked to sing after supper, so they needed an accompanist. At least once every day we sang completely through *The Sound of Music*. Kathy seemed to resent the piano. This middle-aged woman had completely withdrawn from the world. She walked stiffly, like a zombie. Her eyes were huge and staring, never recognizing any of us, never registering any emotion. She hadn't spoken since she had been admitted.

One evening as we were singing "Climb Every Mountain," she wandered into the dining room. She seemed agitated. Several people tried to get her to join us. She pulled back. But we could feel the turmoil locked behind that blank exterior. As we finished the song, I looked at Kathy and let my fingers drift to "In the Garden." Quietly, but with assurance, Kathy began to sing. Everyone stood, silently, listening to the hymn. "And He walks with me, and He talks with me, and He tells me I am His own . . ." Tears flowed. Nurses rushed for charts to record this response. Orderlies cleared their throats and turned their heads. When the song was finished, Kathy left the room.

I played "In the Garden" over and over during the next two weeks but with no results. When I was discharged, Kathy hadn't spoken another word. But she had responded. And if she could do it once, she would do it again. There was hope.

Hope—such an important word, but such an evasive, tenuous feeling. We all felt warmth as we were a part of Kathy's breakthrough. Encouraged by her response, the staff and patients renewed their efforts. But there were times when we saw a friend take a step backward. Times when we all worked but could not reach the person. We watched each other caught in hell and were frustrated because we couldn't discover the expression to lessen the suffering.

One afternoon as we were finishing lunch, Sally, my roommate, heard a song on the radio that brought back painful memories. She burst into tears and in trying to get away from the sound she upset her tray. Others, fighting against intense emotions, began screaming, throwing trays, pushing over chairs and tables. Quickly the staff moved in and sent us to our rooms. Some were given injections. We were all made to lie on our beds. The rest of that day we were quiet, frightened by how quickly we had lost control, appalled by how much progress could be lost when for a few minutes we neglected to try.

Kim was allowed to go home for Thanksgiving, the only patient granted that holiday privilege. She had first bath that morning, and we watched as she dressed in street clothes. Brenda combed Kim's hair. We wished Kim a good day, telling her we would expect her back in the evening to share it with us. As she left with her parents, we waved. She was representing each of us. Her success would partly be ours.

The rest of us had turkey for lunch. Practically everyone had visitors. The entire floor was gay with a holiday spirit.

About 4:00 the door was unlocked. Kim was led in crying. She had been home less than an hour when the walls closed in and she yielded to the compulsion to run. They found her two miles away, still running. Her parents left the Thanksgiving dinner, closed the door of the beautiful colonial house and brought their daughter back.

We crowded around her. "Why? Kim, why?"

She didn't answer the question, only shook her head. She couldn't. She didn't know the answer—yet.

Someone put her arms around her and held her close.

She murmured into the shoulder, "I'm sorry. You all believed in me and I let you down."

The next day Kim was her bright cheerful self. She was back

where she felt safe. The world with its problems and responsibilities was outside. Here on this floor she could live.

Four weeks later she spent a complete day at home before she had to go back to the hospital. Hope. First there—then gone. But always coming back stronger and more enduring.

Carrie, when her thieving became a nuisance, was tied into a rocking chair. We walked by her room looking straight ahead, but she saw each passerby.

"Any whiskey for Carrie?" she called.

Soon she learned to rock and scoot. Then the chair was creeping up and down the halls. Next she was maneuvering it into rooms and candy was again missing. When Carrie was untied, we all felt better. For all of us bound inside by invisible chains, seeing Carrie's outward bonds was too painful a reminder.

We were each a part of the other. No one here had to run a household. No one rushed to a job. No meetings, no telephones, no need for pretense and social graces. Nothing was required of us except beginning to understand ourselves and helping one another.

We had time. Time to sit with a person, silently holding his hand. Time to put rollers into the hair of a woman who wasn't well enough to hold a roller herself. Time to hear a man tell of goals never reached, of the pain of failure, of not providing for his family as he felt he should, while he chain-smoked cigarettes to keep from having to ask an orderly for a light each time. Time to sit by a bed and wipe away the tears of an old woman as she reached back and called for her mother to come to her during this time of loneliness. Time to walk back and forth, back and forth, in a hall, while a young boy struggled against problems he was old enough to feel but not mature enough to solve. Time to read in people's eyes the pleas, "See me. Love me. Know I'm alive and have feelings."

Many of us were here because outside the world had not had the time to meet any of these needs. We had wandered, lost, in a life too busy to notice us. Now we had come to this place called a psychiatric ward, where men and women had been trained to recognize needs—men and women who knew they must discipline and direct, be patient but not indulgent, sympathetic but not pitying, stern but gentle.

Here other people could say to us, "I know. I understand how you feel."

Here men and women didn't live behind masks any more, ashamed to show emotion and express real feelings. They reached out for one another physically and mentally.

Humor, love, compassion, tears, anger, patience, and, most of all, hope were present in that home. And we who were on the locked side of the door did not feel locked in. We felt the world had been locked out.

Fifty to sixty percent of the healing process attributed to this unique relationship.

The person standing on the street looking up at the heavy screened windows need not feel guilty. He has just answered a cry for help. He has provided a place where recovery is possible. These temporary locks may provide the key to unlocking the inward prison that is preventing that member of his family from living a full and productive life.

4

Dear Mommy

Dear Mommy,

We are making something in school for Christmas for the other boys and girls. Hurry and get well so you can come home to us. The kittens are fine.

Love,
Tammy

Dear Mom,

I hope you don't mind me using your stationery.
We went to piano lessons and I got all stars.
I called Caroline and thanked her for cooking our supper. (She always gets so upset.)
I hope you're feeling fine. Bye now.

Kisses,
Leanne

Dear Mother,

I caught 2 muskrats so far. I got 75¢ for one and 35¢ for the other. It was water-soaked. Get well soon, because it's not the same without you.

> Love,
> Mark

P.S. I'm doing real good in English.

Nov. 21, 1967

Went to the dentist. It didn't hurt. I got 3 fillings filled. I helped the Sunday school teacher deliver the canned goods to the poor family.

> Love,
> Craig

Dear Mom,

Lanny took care of us today. Yesterday we had Thanksgiving dinner at Raymont's. Their grandma is real nice.

I'm making you something with my sewing set. I'll send it with Dad to the hospital.

I'm still working on my science notebook.

We haven't started Christmas shopping. We've never done it without you.

> With lots of love,
> Leanne

P.S. I write sloppy. I can't control my writing (right ha ha) hand.
P.P.S. I can't think of anything to say, but I hate to stop writing. Goodbye.

Dear Mommy,

We fingered painted today. I played with Ginny's cat.

> Love,
> Tammy Sue Smith

Dear Mom,

Sunday we went to Balbo's. Mrs. Balbo did Tammy's and my hair. We had Lazonia to eat.

I got my science book done.

I was elected altranate for student council. Today's Ginny's birthday. Dad is getting her a present.

Looking forward to your letter.

Love,
Leanne

Dear Kids,

Thank you for your letters. I'm glad to get them. My medicine makes my hand shake but I'll try to write.

I'm feeling better. It helped to see Daddy and to get your pictures. You are good-looking kids. The other patients say so too.

Everyone in church must be helping you.

Mark, you won't get rich if you only get 2 muskrats.

Leanne, you do a good job writing. I'm glad your science book is finished.

Craig, are you practicing the piano? I play here.

Tammy, do you like Ginny? Does she spoil you?

I'm watching the Santa Claus parade on TV. Our Thanksgiving dinner is at 12:00.

I'm tired now. Have a good day.

Mommy

Now, almost three years later, I wondered what would stand out in the children's minds from my time of hospitalization. I asked them to try to think back and remember how they felt. Craig and Tammy were able to express themselves on paper easily, perhaps because their feelings of insecurity at that time were basic. Leanne and Mark found it more difficult to put into words how they felt. They both admitted to being "confused."

I didn't know specifically what was wrong with my mother at the time she entered the hospital. I only knew she kept losing her temper more often. But I thought it was just because she contracted a disease.

My father didn't talk much about it, but he visited her about every night. Women from the church cleaned the house and neighbors brought in food. Everyone was helpful and concerned. I felt sorry my mother had gone to the hospital but I knew it was necessary for her to be treated and cured.

Mark

The day my mom went to the hospital she was going down to our church to get some stencils so I could do my science notebook. Since I couldn't get them then, I was upset and asked my sixth grade teacher if I could have extra time to do mine. She said I couldn't because it wouldn't be fair to everyone else. Then I told her the reason why I didn't have it done and she gave me three extra days. After that she asked me how my mom was. I was glad she asked.

Every night we had either the neighbor's or church people's specialties or TV dinners. On Thanksgiving day we were going to have turkey TV dinners but then some friends invited us to their house for dinner.

When my mom was going to come home I was afraid of how we should act, but after she got home I went to the grocery and every place she went. She needed me and I helped her.

Leanne

I didn't know what was going on. I didn't know why my mom was in the hospital. Daddy said it was a nervous breakdown. But I didn't know what that was. I asked him, "Will she die?" He didn't answer. And I was scared.

I couldn't sleep at night. I'd come down and Dad would rock me. I remember his stiff white shirt when I laid my cheek down. I cried on it.

Dad was at work during the day and there was no one to talk to. I would hold the cats for someone to love.

Then Daddy said Mom was coming home. He said she would look different and we shouldn't stare. He said she would have a double chin. I didn't know what that meant. I was scared but even so I slept better that night.

When I came home from school the next day Mom was on the love seat. She didn't look any different to me. She was my mom. But when she saw us, she cried.

Craig

Every night I cried myself to sleep. I was always sick in my tummy. I didn't want to go to school. I wanted to stay home with Ginny.

One day I made a mistake and went to Ginny's house after school instead of my house. Ginny wasn't there. She was at my house. I was alone there and scared. Ginny finally found me. I was glad to see her.

Mommy's being sick was the time of a big sad. A big capital letter SAD.

Tammy

5

Home again!

At Christmas time I was discharged from the hospital. During the season of the year when people are caught up in the whirl of shopping, baking, decorating, meeting friends, our house, in contrast, was silent. I do not remember coming home and meeting my children after being separated those weeks. I don't even recall leaving the hospital. I have come to refer to the Christmas of 1967 as "the Christmas I will never remember."

Shock treatments affect individuals in different ways. For some, the temporary amnesia is immediately effective. Even the treatments themselves are a part of the void in memory. For others, the amnesia is postponed or never does manifest itself in a noticeable way. I was able to remember and to retain a great deal of my hospital experiences. As I described in Chapter 3, many of the people made strong impressions upon me. However, a few months after my release, a woman telephoned and identified herself as one of the patients who had been with me and I wasn't able to recall her name, her face, or any association with her, so there may have been many of the hours at the hospital I did not retain. And the weeks immediately following my dismissal are completely blank.

We soon learned that my seemingly rapid improvement in the hospital was false. Getting attention and leaving my responsibilities gave me relief, but ahead of me was still the long process of recovery. I began to slip into the worst period of my illness.

This chapter describing it will be brief and disjointed. It is taken from a few scant notes from that time and from what my family has told me.

Jim took me Christmas shopping that year. Since Jim is a busy executive, and a person who hates shopping, it had always been my responsibility to buy all of the gifts. That year, he held my hand and led me through the stores. He purchased the children's presents as I looked on. Months later I would remark about a certain blouse or shirt and be told that it had been a Christmas present. It seemed strange to be credited with having bought an article I couldn't remember seeing before.

I'm told we had an old-fashioned tree that year, a tree decorated with ropes of cranberries and popcorn. Stringing these had been "busy" work for my hands. The next year when I unpacked the Christmas decorations, I found a paper sack of crushed ornaments. As I pulled them out in bewilderment, Craig said, "You made those last year. We starched string for you, and you wound it around little balloons." I discarded the useless decorations, wondering about the clumsy hands that had made them.

I know those weeks will never return to me. It would be useless to dwell upon them. Because of the success of the treatments, my mind had been given its needed rest.

There are times even today that events of my childhood or even events of yesterday elude me. It is sometimes frustrating not to be able to connect a name with a face or not to remember the recipe for a dessert I supposedly took to a potluck dinner, when I don't even remember the dinner. But it has never frightened me to have the weeks around that Christmas blotted out of my mind. I have, however, found it easier to admit my difficulties and rely on another person to supply the facts than to grope. Most people, middle-aged and older, have their own memory lapses and are quite willing to tell me again details and dates without taking offense.

That Christmas the women's organization at church baked cookies for us. There were so many that they were put in our freezer. They provided treats for the children for several months. Even after I was beginning to be aware, they were still being brought from their cache and enjoyed. I don't remember what we had for Christmas dinner. Jim says the whole family helped, and we did have a holiday meal.

I attended church to listen to the Christmas choir program I had been preparing for when I broke down. I sat quietly, occasionally cueing and directing the choirs from my seat. They say the next time I went to church, I burst into tears and had to be taken out. After that I stopped attending. We didn't go to the family dinner over the holidays, and they say I had the flu in January and spent several days in bed. I don't know. If I could say I remember anything of that time it would be, "I wish I were back in the hospital!"

Coming out of the hospital was a tremendous shock. I had become accustomed to having everything done for me. I had been protected from making decisions, even to having to make my own bed or fix my meals. I have learned since of hospitals equipped with kitchens where the patient is encouraged to cook his own breakfast and clean up afterwards, and to care for his own room. Doctors are also allowing trial home visits, noting the patient's ability to adapt. Thus by gradually introducing various responsibilities, the patient's return to the home atmosphere is not as abrupt and traumatic.

I had no such background. I was transferred from the sheltered existence of the hospital back into a home situation that meant cleaning, cooking, laundry, a ringing telephone, and four children to care for. Unable to cope with even the noise and confusion, much less the routine, I regressed. I withdrew farther from the world of reality than I had at any time during my illness. This deep depression was like being in a windowless room with the walls and ceiling closing in. I was smothering under a great weight that seemed to be pressing on my chest.

In the hospital I had played the piano every day. At home it was to be a year before I even had a desire to touch the keys of my own piano.

In the hospital I had attempted to knit; now the knitting bag was taken out of my sight. I refused to pick up the needles and try, and I became antagonistic when anyone encouraged me.

In the hospital I set my hair every morning and put on lipstick and perfume in anticipation of visiting hours; now I couldn't even be encouraged to comb my hair or put a robe on over my shapeless flannel nightgown.

In the hospital I had picked up magazines and at least read the words under the illustrations; now it tired me to hold the book, and I read the same line over and over without comprehension.

In the hospital I talked to people, even listening and trying to help them with their problems; now I was silent, too tired to speak to my family.

The regression frightened my family. Would I continue to slide away from them? How could they reach me? Would I be returned to the hospital? If so—for how long would it be this time?

They led me from bed, to the table to eat, to the living room to sit, back to the bed to sleep, learning to show patience and love and to disguise worry and discouragement.

I lay on the love seat, on my side, with my legs drawn up and my fists clenched—fighting for every breath. Depression is *hell*. There is no other feeling like it that I can use for comparison. Only the person who has experienced it can understand it. It defies description to the healthy.

Out of habit, the children still came to me with things like, "Where are my boots?" or "Can I go to Pammy's house?" Every question meant a decision. And no matter how trivial that decision, it brought panic. My only answer was, "I don't know."

I wanted to go back to the hospital. Direct orders were so much simpler. They meant only obedience. Someone else had the responsibility of decisions.

It seemed as if I already had more than I could cope with but before I could learn to gulp capsules to take away daily pressures, the doctor began to cut my medication. He did not want to give me a crutch and thus foster a permanent cripple. My mental health was not to be from a bottle, it was to come from within me.

As the effects of the medicine wore off, I would be more aware of the world around me. My family worried whether I could cope with it or would continue to lie on the love seat, my face and ears covered, my mind avoiding reality.

I have a picture of myself that was taken on that Christmas morning. I can see in it the apathy of the woman, eyes empty and unseeing, hands listless in her lap. In front of her are Craig and Tammy holding out gifts to be "oh-ed" and "ah-ed" over, their faces bright and smiling, alight with their belief in Santa Claus. The woman is not responding, not even aware of their needing her attention and approval. It is difficult for me to believe I was that woman.

Often I have thought back to that time and repeated the phrase "A little child shall lead them." During the many hours of those first few months, Mark, Leanne, Craig, and Tammy sat with me on an unscheduled watch. They took turns sitting on the floor holding the hand I dropped limply over the edge of the love seat. Their patient vigil is my first recollection of love.

The Christmas of 1967 was "the Christmas I'll never remember." But it was during that Advent season that the woman I am striving to be today was conceived. Thus it may prove to be my most remembered holy season.

6

This is progress?

I s cowering in fear, under the bedclothes, better than sitting listless on a chair?

Is crying twelve hours a day better than restrained silence?

Is angry frustration better than docile obedience to orders?

I didn't think so. And I believe my recovery was slowed because I didn't know what changes to expect in my personality. Just as the symptoms of a breakdown are similar, there is also a similarity in the steps of recovery. And because the steps often appear to be regression rather than progression, the patient and the family are bewildered and discouraged by change.

I needed someone to say, "Rejoice! Crying means you have won one more battle. You are returning to the world of reality. You hate the way you are, and in your frustration to change that image you are fighting in the only way you know how—with tears." Maybe then I would have recognized them for tears of victory, rather than being ashamed of them, thinking they were tears of weakness and defeat.

There is no time-line of recovery for a mental breakdown. No one can promise how long any person will remain in a certain stage. Some people have assured me that they practically bounded from withdrawal to complete recovery. Others have admitted to plodding for months and even years, and still others have confessed, with sorrow, that they reached a certain stage and never advanced again.

52

Each patient is an individual with his own environment, background, personality, and set of problems. He can receive either love or rejection from those around him, be a fighter or a whiner, have excellent psychiatric care or none at all. All we are sure of is that love, understanding, and knowledge contribute to progress!

If withdrawal is the break from reality then we can also consider withdrawal the beginning of recovery. For me, withdrawal was a period of about three months when I did not communicate with my family and did not interest myself in any activity, either mental or physical. I broke from the world of responsibility, the world of problems and decisions, the world that represented tragedy and disappointment. It was a time of constant physical and mental agony. My arms and legs were like weights hung on my body, making it virtually impossible to walk or hold any object. My head felt heavy and numb, too large for my body. My thought processes were laggardly. A tremendous weight lay on my chest, making every breath an effort. I had only one certain thought, that I was going to smother. Deep depression is the most powerful of invisible prisons. It holds you helpless in a suffocating, locked cell.

My family adjusted to my lying down or sitting quietly wherever they placed me. They lived around me, deciding it was useless to include me in any discussions or activity. But because I acted only under order I was not a difficult patient to care for.

Then one morning I refused to get out of bed. I covered my head with the blankets, shutting out the light of day. If it remained night, I would not have to get out of bed. And if I did not get out of bed, I would not have to decide which dress to put on. Jim and the children were upset. I was panicked. I had been able to sit in the living room, wearing my nightgown, and stare at the television. Why was I now cowering in bed afraid to open my closet door?

I didn't know then that what I was experiencing was my first acceptance of the world around me. I had admitted to being a part of a world that involved such decisions as what dress to wear. I was no longer entirely passive. Even though I couldn't meet this first challenge, I knew it was there.

When Jim understood the reason for my fear, rather than chide me or belittle me, he went to my closet and chose a dress. "Here," he said, "put this on."

Together, the six of us moved into one more of our series of adjustments. We learned that my seeing a problem, however small, and my solving it, were two different things. I looked timidly around me and was overwhelmed.

Jim realized that everything couldn't be done for me or I would never be independent. But he also knew I couldn't be left alone, in fear, with a task beyond my ability. Each situation would require an individual solution. Each person would have to watch me closely. They would each have to decide when the situation called for waiting and when it called for the patient words, "I'll help you."

Jim reminded himself and the children, "we must never offer our help with reluctance or anger, or with the accusation, 'You can do it yourself if you really want to.' "

To work with me, an illogical patient, they would all have to be mature and logical themselves. Was this beyond the ability of children? Or even for Jim as an adult?

Until that time of indecision, I didn't realize how much of life is based on the ability to make a decision. I couldn't clean the house. Which room would I start in? Should I dust first or run the vacuum cleaner?

I wasn't able to do the laundry. Should I drop that towel in with the underwear or should it go in with the sheets?

I couldn't cook. When I opened the cupboard doors, a variety of food stared back at me, challenging me to make a decision and plan a menu.

I couldn't grocery shop. Should I buy hot cereal or cold? Cold? Then which brand? Large box or small? Sugared or plain? Every task ended with my sitting down while waves of depression swelled within me. I clenched my fists as indecision brought on a guilty conscience which resulted in a deeper conviction of "I can't!"

Just as Jim stepped in and helped me choose a dress, the family helped me cope with other decisions. Large jobs were broken down into smaller ones. When I couldn't decide whether to vacuum or dust, Mark put the dustcloth in my hand and went for the sweeper himself. The problem of whether to dust the piano or the table first, however, was mine to solve.

Leanne helped sort the laundry. If she noticed my standing too long with a piece of clothing in my hand, she pointed to the correct pile and continued her own sorting. At the market, I pushed the cart and she dropped in the groceries. At mealtime, they cooked and I set the table. I was busy, included in the routine work, but I was most certainly one of the laborers and a long way from becoming the "boss."

I was staying alone now while the children were in school and Jim at work. I did not need constant supervision and there were even simple tasks I was able to accomplish alone. I could pull the sheets and spread up on the bed, though the thought of changing the sheets was still staggering. I could put the cups and plates in the dishwasher after breakfast. Beyond that, I usually preferred sitting down. I knew I should keep busy, but it was such an effort. As I sat there, I felt guilty, which increased my depression which made it more impossible to get up out of my chair. This is when Lanny, my next-door neighbor, began helping me.

Lanny would drop in every morning about 9:00 for a cup of coffee. She told me, recently, that she knew what kind of day I was having by my eyes. When they were vacant, I was going to sit; when they were wild I was going to be argumentative and short of patience; if they were calm, she had hopes that I could accomplish something.

Lanny had learned patience while working at a nursing home as an aide. Other than tending those bedfast, elderly people she had had no special schooling or training in handling the mentally ill. She simply used her common sense. While we had our coffee she always asked me what had to be done that day. If I mumbled, "Ironing," she would say, "All right, I'll give you until noon to finish it. I'll check back then to see how you're doing."

She was never certain when she returned how she would find me. I might still be at the kitchen table with the cup of coffee cold in front of me. I might have put up the ironing board but been unable to finish even the first piece. Or she might be surprised and find I had completed the basket of clothes. If this was the case, she praised me (sensibly, not gushing, as we often overpraise a child for a reasonable accomplishment) and asked, "What else has to be done?"

If she found me sitting, she plugged in the iron and talked to me while she worked, never condemning me or showing her disap-

pointment. When she had finished, she suggested a new job, a new
time limit, and left. Thus I began to know the satisfaction of one
job accomplished without the burden of several failures.

I had to remind myself to move slowly. My overall progress was
tediously slow and I was likely to become overconfident following
an accomplishment. Because of this, success often brought disaster.
I would cook a simple meal and be so proud that I would begin
planning and scheduling projects for the future. The plans would
turn into worry and the worry into depression, and I would be back
staring into space with my fists clenched in my lap. I could become
hopelessly discouraged in April thinking about what I would take
to the family reunion in August. I had to discipline myself to concentrate only upon the present.

We found that if I did become tied up over a trivial thing such
as this and it grew out of proportion, my thoughts had to be diverted.
Dwelling upon any subject too long was a detriment to my mental
outlook. A short trip in the car, watching a TV program that was
not overemotional, working in the flower beds, were all therapy.
Reading had always been my tool for relaxation, but now I couldn't
follow the plot line, and I usually lost interest and laid the book
or magazine aside. Leanne found the solution. She brought home
books from her grade-school library and encouraged me to reread
some of my childhood favorites. I began on the Laura Wilder pioneer
series. This simpler writing and the shorter books were easier to
understand and once again I was able to laugh and cry with fictional
characters.

Thus I learned to face each morning, slowed down, uncertain,
often reluctant, and still stifled by depression, but at least facing
the day rather than hiding under blankets, hoping for perpetual night.

The next stage I encountered was unfounded fear. A fear springing
from a terrifying circumstance is justifiable, but even more frightening
is a fear for which you cannot give a reason. It is always with you
and you cannot explain it away or remove the cause.

I was simply afraid. I wanted to hide behind our big orange
wing-backed rocker with my arms hugged around my head. It seemed
that hidden in that corner I would be safe. Yet I was also afraid
to give in to that compulsion because I was afraid if I did, something
dreadful would happen to me.

I never wanted to be alone, so I nagged my family for constant attention. I needed to touch someone all the time. Mark began getting up earlier for school to sit with me as we watched dawn come into the living room. Craig, always the sensitive one, held my hand and stroked my face. Tammy carried stacks of picture books into the living room and read to me the ones she had memorized. They had no idea what might soothe me. They just kept trying new things, each searching in his own way.

I became very adept at writing absence excuses to the school. I had begun keeping a different child home with me every day. Each morning I could find an ailment or complaint that, if encouraged, turned into a sufficient reason for them to be absent. They had quite a series of colds, sore throats, and flu that spring. I did not feel guilty at their missing classes. I needed someone with me, and I believed that they were actually sick. Of course, they were happy to agree with me and have a vacation every fourth day of school. They took turns holding my hand while we watched television.

Jim discovered what I was doing and firmly ordered the children to get ready and leave for school and ignore my pleas. He explained to me that I could not perpetually have companionship, that I would have to learn independence. So I tried to control my panic. When I would have preferred to stay safely closed in the house, I forced myself to venture outside of the house. I tried to run errands that I had previously postponed until Jim or one of the children could accompany me. A drive to the drugstore a few blocks away was accomplished only after many false starts.

One afternoon I gritted my teeth and vowed I would do the grocery shopping. I chose a familiar market close to home and a time when I hoped they would not be too busy. I pushed my cart over to the first aisle and began making my selections. Cereal—butter—eggs—cold meat. Other women went past me, shopping quickly, with assurance. I pushed my cart nearer the side of the aisle to be out of their way.

At the end of the aisle I sighed. I had made it that far. I rounded the end of Aisle 1 and faced Aisle 2. It stretched endlessly, the shelves towering over me seemingly stacked with thousands of cans of vegetables and fruits. The sweat from my palms made the handle so slippery, I had trouble hanging onto the cart. How could I move through that jeering jungle of containers?

A bell rang, the signal that a carry-out boy was needed in the front. It kept ringing, the sound amplifying in my head. Someone bumped into me. Voices rose in bedlam. The background music grew loud. I couldn't do it. I walked into the pyramids of cans, put my hands over my ears, and shut my eyes.

I was fortunate. A woman I knew found me cowering there. Gently she led me through the store and out to my car. At home, I shut the door and savored the silence.

I realized then that part of my fear was change. When I adjusted to a situation, I was in control, but when the place or circumstances changed, I couldn't adapt. When the children left for school, it took me quite awhile to feel comfortable in silence, yet when they burst through the door in the afternoon, I didn't want their noise. I didn't want to stay alone, but if we went out, I clutched Jim's arm in terror of the noise and confusion. When it was time to come back home, fear grew inside me. Home meant lunch to fix, clothes to change. Why couldn't things stay the same? Why was life such a complicated parade of change?

I had to learn to govern my day. I could not expose myself to a series of adaptations, stimulations, or multiple demands on my attention. Neither could I hide in a cocoon. Each day had to be a balance of social contact and solitude with the opportunity to withdraw from either if it proved too difficult. I could not yet commit myself to obligations in the future. I had to live each hour as it came.

My hands often trembled, wanting something to occupy them. I had more of the appearance now of what we think of as a "nervous" person. I paced the floor. My hands fluttered. I was easily excitable.

One Sunday my parents drove the 140 miles to visit me, and I spent the afternoon picking up minute pieces of lint from the carpet. I could not sit down. I couldn't converse with them. I had to keep moving. It seemed perfectly logical to me. Why couldn't they understand that if I didn't pick up the lint I would have to climb behind the orange chair and escape from them altogether?

These fears were heralding another step of recovery. Not only had I accepted the world of reality, I was now conscious of my inability to function in it. I had looked into our full-length mirror and had seen a woman who disgusted me. I could remember having dreams and goals. I knew I had a talent for writing and for music. I had entertained guests and been active in many projects. I didn't want to be the fearful, indecisive, slovenly woman who was looking back at me from the mirror. What could I do about it? It was this frustration that began my period of continual tears. Twelve hours a day I cried. It was during this time that I held Leanne and cried out, "I'm crazy. I don't want to be crazy, but I am crazy!"

This was a new and strange Nancy. Before my illness I rarely cried. My angers, hurts, and disappointments had always been hidden inside (which was part of my problem—the inability to express emotions). Only a sullen silence let my family know when I was battling a problem. Now I was behaving like a petulant child. It seemed to them that I was using tears only to get my own way and to gain sympathy. Patience is difficult to practice in the face of such tantrums.

They became glum as I became loudly irrational.

I despised contradiction. It seemed to me that constantly some superior-acting person was calmly repudiating everything I said. Why did they believe it was a kindness to me to continually reassure me that I wasn't really sick, and if I was a good girl this would all go away? But I was ready to fight the world if need be. I had a few battle cries of my own. "I am sick!" "I can't do that!" "I'm crazy!" "You don't know how I feel, so don't say you understand!" "Leave me alone!" "Shut up. All of you shut up."

Not a very easy person to love.

No wonder the door often closed sharply in my face and I found myself alone with my only solace the never-ending tears.

Psychologists tell us that man has proved that he can endure practically any torture or circumstance if he knows that there will be an end to it. I'm confident that we six people trying to live together could have handled this tumultuous period with more patience and hope if we had known it would end. But at the time we were living it, it seemed that there had never been or ever would be any world but this one of raised voices awash with tears.

Even without such assurance we did eventually adjust. The family stopped being alarmed at their failure to please me and so stopped asking me, "What is wrong?" I was relieved to no longer have to say, "I don't know," because there was no other answer. I continued to function while the tears fell sizzling into the frying pan and dropped onto the dresses as I ironed. Without having constantly to defend my behavior I stopped being rebellious and gradually experienced periods of calm.

I knew I had conquered another step when I met a woman who patted my arm and said, "You're just blue. I know exactly how you feel, I've had blue days myself. We all have it. You'll get over it."

As usual blood rushed to my head. She didn't know how I felt!

But, for the first time, I thought before I struck out. I thought, she really believes she's being kind. Their clichés are as empty of thought as those murmured to the family who stands at the casket of a relative. They don't know what to say and they feel helpless. With much effort I swallowed my anger and said, "Thank you for your encouragement."

I had finally seen someone else's point of view. I had broken the pattern of always thinking only of myself.

Life for us now took on a semblance of normality. I was usually able to function in public without betraying the inner turmoil. More and more I was quietly fighting the enemies of indecision, guilt, and fear while I was alone. If I stayed calm I was now able to rule them. They were losing some of their hold on my mind and body.

One morning I awoke before Jim did. Something was very different. I lay looking about the room, seeing the familiar furniture, watching the blue gray of dawn come in the north window, but afraid to move for fear I would destroy this sensation or worse yet awake and find it all a dream.

Jim moved and opened his eyes. I whispered. "It's gone."

Sometime during the night, the depression that had gripped me for so many months had disappeared! My body was light. My mind was free. The day before me appeared as a blessing rather than a punishment. I rose, anxious to experiment. I greeted the children with a smile, fixed their breakfasts, and made the beds. I literally felt like rolling up my sleeves and pitching in—not only into the housework but into life.

At the end of the day I curled around Jim's back in bed, tired and content. I promised him, "I'll never go back there again."

We decided the next day I would accompany him on a business trip. We would be driving all day and would have lunch, just the two of us, to celebrate. We fell asleep happy.

The next morning depression was back.

I was bitter. How could I have slipped back? I had gone to sleep happy; why should I wake this way? The trip that had been planned as a celebration turned out to be just another "therapy trip."

All of my symptoms returned that day. I found it difficult to breathe in the car. The air seemed stuffy and close. I clung to the door and huddled on my side of the seat in fear. At the restaurant I couldn't choose anything from the menu. I pleaded with Jim to order for me and tell the waitress. I didn't want to talk to anyone. I felt cheated. Why did I have this setback?

It was another two weeks before I had another "good day." I knew it could be brief, so I made the most of it, enjoying every moment of my freedom, but at the same time steeled for the recurrence of depression.

I learned to watch for what I called my "guilty conscience feeling." It is like the feeling all of us have when we have hurt someone or done something wrong. It was a feeling I had had since childhood and from which I suffered now. I would often awake feeling as though in my sleep I must have committed a heinous crime. When I explained it to my doctor, he understood and suggested, "Either go back to sleep for about twenty minutes and when you wake again it will be gone, or else busy yourself with something until it goes away." Beyond this he had no explanation for this sensation.

His suggestions worked. And I also used this guilty feeling as a warning signal of possible trouble ahead. I would admit to Jim when I felt it, and we all knew we should be cautious until we saw how well I was going to be able to handle this symptom of depression.

Even though we all felt close to victory now, we knew, as with every other stage, success would not be instantaneous. It would take time and work. When I became discouraged, Jim would remind me, "The doctor, the kids, and I are doing all we can, but you have to fight. We can only help you. Unless you fight every day, every hour, you'll stay on this plateau and never reach the top."

I was tired. Why not stop fighting? I would just quit and stay "the odd Mrs. Smith." It would be peaceful to be left alone to watch television or read a book. Maybe if I quit, people would stop making these impossible demands on me.

Then I would pick up a magazine that had once carried an article I had written or I would hear a choir singing an anthem I had conducted, and I wanted to know accomplishments again. I tried to play the intricate runs of Bach, but I couldn't. I tried to put an idea on paper but it came out in confusion. I watched the children growing up. I wanted to be a part of their successes and a comfort to them in the failures. Just existing wasn't enough. I wanted to live! I had nearly lost everything. I knew how important it was.

With determination I began stringing together hours of health. I was beginning to have faith in myself, in other people, and once again in a spiritual deity. I was thankful for each hour that I was free of depression and tried to find the thoughts or circumstances that brought the good days and the danger that signaled the bad ones.

We had hope. As it encouraged my progress, the entire family responded with raised spirits. At times we had been in danger of permanent alienation from one another. We had each gone through our own "valley of shadows." For those two years the family foundation had been in danger. One person could have quit, walked out, or simply shut himself away from the problem, and the foundation could have crumbled. But we were making it! We were walking out the other side still holding one another's hands. Mental illness had struck us, but we were proving to be stronger than the hell it brought with it. We felt we had every right to rejoice.

Like an invalid getting accustomed to using his legs, I gently began exercising my mind and emotions. I asked Jim to take me to see the movie *Charly*. He hesitated because the theme was mental retardation. He wasn't sure this was a wise choice of movies. We asked another couple to go with us and I knew Jim was nervous during the opening scenes. I did identify with many of the problems of Charly but I enjoyed the movie. Later, however, when we stopped for a sandwich, I was surly and argumentative. The adjustment from the fantasy of a film story to conversation with three other people was too difficult. I should not have tried to combine the two experiences in one evening.

Another evening we attended a business dinner. Jim's associates were surprised in the change in me. Many of them said, "It's good to have the old Nancy back again." I didn't say that I felt this was an entirely new Nancy, one better equipped to face life. I understood what they meant, and merely agreed, "She's glad to be back."

After the dinner, several people invited us to go with them to a small club that was featuring a trombone player. In less than ten minutes the sound amplified and I felt my features freeze and tighten. I had to be taken home. I had learned that I could not tolerate loud noise and couldn't concentrate on multiple conversations.

I rejoined a Christian service organization (FISH) that I had done volunteer work for prior to my breakdown. One of my first calls was to talk to a despondent widow. I stayed two hours and drove home content. I had forgotten myself and helped someone else.

The Sunday morning adult discussion group had always been one of my favorite dialogue groups. I began attending again. I argued with the teacher and twice burst into tears. Subjects of controversy and philosophy were still too taxing.

Sometimes I succeeded, sometimes I failed, but I was learning my abilities and my limitations.

I wrote and sold a children's story. The doctor encouraged my writing. He said it was a healthy escape into a make-believe world. It relaxed my tensions and a sale was an ego-builder.

I gave up having dinner guests. The pressure of cooking and keeping order was too much.

Elected secretary of the Writer's Guild, I found I could write letters and keep minutes.

Then came my first invitation to stand before a roomful of people and share with them my experience of the past two years. Could I organize and deliver a speech on temporary mental illness with enough ability to enlighten them? Most of my friends were reluctant to have me take on such a responsibility. Jim refused to make the decision for me. I took the question to my doctor and we talked it out. His advice: "Of course. Even if you can't give a polished lecture, just letting them look at you will help them realize you are healthy and not ashamed to have experienced a breakdown."

I accepted the invitation. Other than the few butterflies everyone feels when his name is on the program, I had no qualms that night.

I realized my behavior could never be prejudged, not even by me. I had to experiment. I tried not to be frightened away from new ventures by cautious outsiders. And I tried not to use my illness as an excuse to avoid distasteful jobs. I was Nancy. What I found rewarding might overwhelm someone else. What to others seemed an easy job could be trouble for me. This was a part of my new independence. I had learned to think for myself and base my decisions on my own conclusions.

Just as I admitted to being mentally and emotionally disturbed, I continued to be honest by thinking of myself still as a mental patient. I was in no hurry to say I was an ex-patient. Perhaps all of my life I would have to be alert to danger signals. I didn't want to return to where I had been.

I was living cautiously—but at least I was once again living.

7

Let's talk about it

I was fortunate to have been put in the care of a doctor I learned to respect and admire. I say learned, because it took several months of patience on his part to get me to respond. My first meeting with him ended with a bold, black, screaming NO! "No, I don't want to be hospitalized. No, there's nothing wrong with me. No, I don't like you. No. No. NO!"

I was fortunate because there are many pitfalls in choosing a psychiatrist.

Electroshock and drugs are used to erase the mind. The easiest way to understand the purpose of shock is to think of a graph with a moving needle. Electroshock shakes the needles into following a new pattern. The graph comes out in a new design. The patient is seeing his old problem in a new way. Some psychiatrists stop here. They give the patient a month's supply of pills and say, "Now you're cured."

But the erasing of the old thinking is only half of the solution. The patient has to begin to write again. And unless he understands his problems and how to cope with them, he will soon be writing the same mistakes. This will eventually bring him back to the hospital as confused as before.

How can a family be sure their doctor will not dismiss their loved one too soon? Or keep the person coming back too long just to receive the money? How does a family choose a psychiatrist?

My doctor said he receives calls every day from people who ask only one question, "What do you charge?" When he tells them his fee, they say, "I know a doctor I can get cheaper." He always suggests they consult the other doctor. He feels he would have little success helping any person who is bargain shopping.

Doctors should not be chosen only by price!

Several people can help the family make the decision. The family medical doctor, a priest, a minister—all have had experience dealing with psychiatrists. They have consulted them on various problems and know them by reputation. They will be able to tell the family some of the background of the available doctors, their methods, and their personality.

The family may talk to individuals who have experienced temporary disorders and get their opinion.

They can call the psychiatrist and make an appointment for a short get-acquainted visit to meet him and ask questions.

Some questions to consider: When the doctor dismisses his patients do they stay well or do they have a tendency to come back again and again?

Is he sympathetic, patting the patient on the back and making promises, or does he believe his role is to teach discipline and encourage the patient to face his problems?

Are his charges based on a visit of fifteen minutes or upon hour sessions?

Does he administer shock?

Does he use drugs? What kind? For how long?

After the family has investigated the available doctors it becomes a personal choice of who and what will meet the needs of the patient. Every person is an individual, and it is important that the doctor be a person whom the *patient* can learn to trust and in whom he can eventually have complete faith. Be cautious! It is better to choose the doctor carefully and stay with him than to confuse the patient by hopping from office to office hoping to find a doctor who peddles miracles. And very important—once the decision has been made, allow the doctor a fair length of time to produce results, because at first the patient will be devious and insincere!

I know, because I tried every tactic in the hospital. After a few days of sulking, I had decided rebellion wasn't the answer. I would charm him. I smiled and said, "Good morning, doctor. How are you today?" My scheme was to trick him into smiling back and we would be friends and I would go home. It didn't work. He came into my room to administer the treatment, growled a "good morning" and left. I hated him.

I kept changing my strategy, but none of my new tactics brought any better results.

After I was dismissed from the hospital, I was scheduled to see the doctor three times a week, one hour each session. They were silent hours because I refused to talk and he wouldn't beg. I sat staring at my hands and he occupied himself by cleaning his pipe or twirling a letter opener.

I broke first. I screamed at him in anger. "What do you want me to say?"

He shrugged his shoulders. "Whatever you feel like saying."

"What should I do?"

"What do you want to do?"

"Let me alone. Just let me alone."

I know now *he* wasn't bothering me. It was *me* beginning to bother me.

I vowed to shock him. I was sick of his blank face, his refusing to react. He had to notice me. Something. A smile—anger—anything! Like a child I sought attention by making up stories. When the first one didn't get a response I tried another one more dramatic than the first.

Nothing.

I cried.

Nothing.

I stuck out my chin. "Don't you even like the way I wear my hair? Doesn't anything please you? Say something. Don't just sit there."

Nothing.

I began rocking in my chair, the motion that I had used to fill many hours in the hospital. I looked at him through tear-flooded eyes and pleaded, "Take me on your lap and rock me."

"Like your daddy used to do?"

"Yes."

"I'm not your daddy and you are not a little girl. Holding you would only make you secure for a little while. I want to help you handle your feelings and fears like a grown woman."

I was finished fighting. He hadn't changed, but I had. His patience had lasted. Accepting a tissue, I blew my nose. With just a slight smile I looked at him for a long time. Pulling together all of the strength I had left, I asked, "Will you help me?"

Just a slight laugh wrinkle around his eyes showed for a second; then the simple answer came in that same impersonal voice. "Yes."

It wasn't a smooth trip. My emotions were unpredictable. Sometimes I entered the office surly, sometimes too gay, in a teasing mood, in depression, up . . . down, open . . . closed. I would meet a big problem head-on, understand it and make a decision; then a little problem would push me into a rage or dissolve me into those ever-present tears.

I made the mistake of trying to relate each session to my husband on the way home. When the doctor found out, he forbade it. He said, "It's difficult enough for you to go through it once. I'm the one who will help you. Don't repeat it or make general conversation of it with other people. They will enjoy the presentation but they probably won't be able to offer you any constructive advice."

I felt better after that. It was easier knowing I could say whatever I needed to say and not have to confess it later to my husband.

We talked. I soon learned that the doctor didn't use words like "bad" and "good". He never condemned me. But then neither did he praise me. He was analyzing me. It was a relief to say "dammit" and "hell" when I was angry. I haven't made these permanent words in my vocabulary, but at that time I found it a surprising relief, and the sky didn't fall in as I had been taught it would if I ever expressed my feelings strongly.

I said how I really felt about people. Thoughts I had repressed for years I expressed. It was great! Out it tumbled week after week. I became accustomed to the doctor's blank face. In fact, I didn't care any more. I was doing this for me, not him. I was doing it because I was emptying myself of hate, fear, and insecurities.

Finally after many months, it was all out. I couldn't think of anything else to say.

The doctor cleared his throat, "Now it's my turn to talk." What followed was startling. I sat open-mouthed while he recapped all that I had told him over the months without consulting a single note! (I later asked him how he did that but he only smiled and refused to answer. I still don't know if this is a talent acquired in training or one with which he was born.) Then he told me things about myself that I *hadn't* told him. He pinpointed exact problems, and finally ended with the question, "What are you going to do about it?"

"Do about it?" My eyes opened wide in surprise. "Why, that's your job. *You* have to tell *me* what to do about it."

"All right, I will. You're too unstable. You have too many ups and downs. You have to operate on a more even line. Not too happy, never too sad."

"Why don't you just perform a lobotomy on me? Then I won't feel anything." I was angry. "I'm Nancy and I like being Nancy. I'm a writer. If I don't go up to the mountaintops and down to the valleys, how can I write about them? I won't do it. You won't change me."

"Okay. I won't change you if you don't want to be changed. But if you want to be Nancy, you have to learn to function as Nancy. You have to know your capacities and limitations. What your danger signals are. How you should react to specific situations."

I sighed and nodded. This, too, was part of it. I had to accept the responsibility of myself. The answers and solutions had to be mine. We began a new phase that I called "Seeing the Problem in Perspective."

Many problems that bothered me had come from my childhood. I was always sensitive, easily hurt and easily feeling rejected. I locked myself inside my playhouse with my make-believe family. I read three and four books a week and became the heroine. Driving the cows to pasture, I stared up at the sky while I wove daydreams and stories of my own. I escaped the real world and made up a better one whenever I needed it. Hurts or punishments that started out very small grew into great adventures in my mind. Slights that others didn't intend gnawed at me because I basked in the romantic tortures I concocted. Now it was time to take them all out and recognize them.

The doctor asked, "What was your first conception of sex?"

I described to him my girlish dream of sitting under a tree in a full, flowered dress, a handsome prince lying there with his head in my lap while I smoothed back his dark hair from his forehead.

"And how do you look at sex today?"

I looked down in my lap and whispered, "The same way."

"What do you call the sexual relationship between your husband and you?"

"Making love."

"Not intercourse?"

I looked up quickly, my cheeks hot. "No!"

"Don't you see, you're still living in your childhood fantasy world. You won't face reality, failure, or ugliness. For you everything must be perfection, a paradise on earth. You've pushed yourself for thirty-two years toward excellence. You never wanted second place. But besides that, you demanded that your friends have the same yardstick. You expect too much of them and they get weary trying to meet your standards. Then when you realize they are weak, you try to manipulate them into being what you imagine they can be. For awhile they try, but when the task becomes too much, they move away from your influence. They have the advantage that they *can* move away. You can't get away from yourself. You drove, pushed, and demanded yourself right into the psychiatric ward!"

As painful as it was to hear these words, I knew I was hearing the truth about myself.

"There is nothing wrong in being human, Nancy. Forgive yourself when you fail. Show compassion to other people when they fail. Understand that there are times when shouted angry words are beneficial, times when sex is not a spiritual union of two people, but an animal release of tensions. You and those around you will be happier for it."

I had to know the answer to one question. "What am I doing to my children? Have I already prohibited them from growing up into healthy adults?"

"To fail in one area doesn't mean you flunk all categories of life. Your role as a mother is healthy. You are very positive about your method of raising your children, and it seems to be a good method."

For that I was grateful. "But what should I do about myself?"

"Your trouble started early in your childhood. Let's go back and relive the episodes that you've told me about. This time you be an adult and view the situation with the insight of maturity."

He restated my childhood incidents inserting Leanne's or Tammy's name in place of mine. Then he asked me as an objective third party to give my opinion. As I faced each of my childhood problems in an adult way, I was amazed to see the fears and guilts crumble and disappear.

Just as it took months to reveal the causes of my breakdown, it also took months to find workable solutions. Again and again I stomped my foot and said, "No, I won't." When I failed in some of his suggestions that I tried, I cried in discouragement. Slowly I understood it wasn't just my world. I couldn't always have my way. Jim had feelings too. He had had a different childhood, different shortcomings, different feelings for failure. In other words, I wasn't always right and he always wrong. I had to look at his point of view and what led him to believe as he did. I was learning to live with myself and other people.

I was tired of trying. It was too much. Results weren't coming as quickly as I wanted. I returned to wheedling the doctor for sympathy. There were days when his lap and the rocking chair still looked comforting and so much easier than this battle I was being forced to fight.

Only this time the doctor wasn't so lenient. "No tears. I can't talk to you when you cry." He resented my silence. "I have other patients. Don't waste my time." He goaded me continually.

One afternoon I couldn't take any more of his criticism and ridicule. I jumped from the chair, my fists clenched, and shouted at him. "I'm going to be someone. Do you hear me? I'm going to be someone!"

He came around the desk and took my raised fists in his hands—his first demonstration of affection—and said, "Yes, I hear you. And now I know you are going to get well."

He had made me fight. Caring for a person can be shown in many ways. He had taken the hard route. As he had said so many months before, "I could treat you like a child, but I want to give you strength to meet life as a woman."

After that the sessions were spaced farther and farther apart. They stretched from every two weeks to once a month, and then to every two months. One day at the end of our talk, he said, "I'm going to move to a new office. When I'm settled, I'll call you for your next appointment."

I never heard from him. He had cut the strings. I know he is as close as the telephone, but as of now I haven't felt the need to call him for security or reassurance.

Because of his kindness in helping me with my first mental illness article, we had a few talks as friend to friend. Those were times when he no longer assumed the impersonal role of doctor. During these talks he told me of some of the problems of his profession. He shook his head, "People wait too long. Many problems could be cleared up in a few visits. As with so many illnesses, the sooner the diagnosis, the shorter the recovery. But people wait for various reasons. Some feel they can handle it themselves. They hope if they ignore the symptoms they will go away. They are ashamed, afraid, embarrassed. They say they can't afford treatment. All are excuses to wait until I have no choice but to hospitalize them and proceed with emergency measures."

He went on. "People expect instant results. One person asked me to use hypnosis and go in and take the sickness out of his brain. Little is known of the human mind, and we doctors are frustrated because we don't have 'sure cures.' I envy the surgeon who is called in the middle of the night to remove an appendix. The patient is in extreme pain, the operation is short, and the patient immediately feels better. The family is happy and pays the fee quickly.

"My patients often see no noticeable results for months. In the meantime they complain. Often the patient quits coming to me and then improves and believes he accomplished it without my help, not realizing that the difficult part had been accomplished as a result of our time together and my knowledge."

He voiced a third regret. "Public ignorance. Mental illness isn't understood so it's feared. To negate the fear the public relies on psychiatrist jokes. We're crucified on our own couch, nailed there with nicknames and smutty stories. Movies make every hospital a snake pit and every doctor a mad scientist. The public recognizes advancement in other fields of medicine but keeps the image of mental illness back in the times of witch-burning."

I could understand some of his frustrations because I could see in my own case and the cases of others that knowledge is very important for the recovery of the patient. If any person in connection with the patient is ignorant, he deters and at times even prevents the recovery of the patient. One woman has failed to recover because her husband has kept her locked in the house away from her friends. The telephone has even been removed. Needless to say, the doctor has failed with her. The family is with the patient more than the doctor, and their negative ideas have prohibited his helping her back to health.

Psychiatry is more than chatting with rich women who are cuddling poodle dogs. It is a difficult challenge for any person. A psychiatrist first completes a two-year premedical course in college. This is followed by four years of medical school and work as an intern for at least one year, at the end of which time he must pass his state board examination to obtain his license to practice. Then come five years of psychiatric study, which includes three years in mental hospitals as a resident doctor in training. Finally he must pass a specialty examination. Only then is he allowed to practice psychiatry.

It is this study and years of dedication that equip him to deal with people's confused minds. He cannot be compared to the charlatan who advertises in the yellow pages that he can heal your life with anything from the stars to a deck of cards. Yet people every day are being taken in by such get-well-quick schemes.

Mornings begin early for the psychiatrist, with a hospital visit to administer treatments and check records. Many hours are spent then in his office listening and *hearing*. He must concentrate completely on the disconnected revelations of each patient. The result of each session is either taped or written into the patient's record. Evening may mean more office hours. He takes his turn on emergency call. He is called out of bed to check every attempted suicide. It's a seven days a week, twelve hours a day job.

I feel my doctor is an example of the dedication of a good psychiatrist. He tried to take a two-week vacation in Florida. After the sun had baked away the first fatigue, he lay on the sand and began to think. His thoughts soon became concern and then worry. These were his patients. They had come to him for help. He had to know how they were. He got up, packed his bags, and came home. I thought this rather a surprising action for a man whose professional caricature is that of an eccentric with a Van Dyke beard who keeps people coming back month after month just to become rich.

After I received the telephone call from *McCall's* magazine, I was anxious for my next appointment. When it was finally my turn, I hurried into the doctor's office, quickly shutting the door behind me. My face must have been radiant. Before I could speak, the doctor grinned, "They bought it!"

I nodded yes, too excited to speak. I opened and shut my hands several times before I decided to obey my impulse. I ran to him, put my arms around his neck, and hugged him. As I did I whispered, "Thank you for making me well!"

When I drew back there were tears on his cheeks. He took the back of his hand and wiped them away. Twice he had to swallow before he could speak. Then he said, "You are my first patient to say thank you."

So each article I write and each time I speak, I am, in part, still saying thank you to one particular doctor, but I'm also saying thank you to the many people dedicating their lives to a difficult and often thankless job—helping people like me talk about their illness.

8

Where have all the people gone?

The drama of my breakdown and unexpected hospitalization soon lost its shock and excitement. Neighbors, alarmed, had responded by sending over casseroles and cakes "to help out." People had mailed get-well cards and ordered flowers. The immediate crisis was met and overcome. For this we will always be grateful.

Then soon after I came home, the telephone stopped ringing, and we found ourselves alone.

Before we had had time to adjust to people's generosity, the wave of attention had come and gone. We realized that we could not depend upon people indefinitely, but we had not prepared ourselves for the wake of silence that followed. We had expected a continuing interest in us as a family. We needed to be able to rely on friendship. What we got, as so many mental patients know, was isolation.

People often say to me now, "But you never said you wanted company. You know I would have come if you had asked." If I had asked. This was putting the responsibility on me. The person who, at the time, was illogical, uncertain, and afraid. It also put me in the position of asking for love. And love is a commodity that withers when it is demanded. Lanny did not wait for me to invite her every morning for coffee. She came. I needed impromptu visits and spontaneous expressions of affection. I was not capable of using the telephone or keeping an appointment book, and, if

I had been, I would not have gone begging by placing an order for attention.

One woman, concerned for a friend of hers who was in the psychiatric ward, called the woman's church to see if anything was being done for her. The secretary said, "I'm sure there is. I'll check and call you back."

Three days later the secretary called and said happily, "I knew we were doing something. We sent a card."

What they didn't even bother to find out about was that the woman's children had been placed in a temporary home, the family was deeply in debt, and the car had broken down.

Sadly, too many people dismiss their obligations to a fellow human being by sending a card!

I remember standing by our picture window watching cars go by. With the approach of each one was the hope that this one would slow and turn into our driveway. The Avon lady, an insurance man, a stranger—anyone who would just take a few minutes of his time to talk. The names of friends and relatives passed through my mind. Didn't any of them care enough to keep in touch?

I wasn't well enough to be understanding and forgiving. I didn't excuse them by saying they had families and duties of their own. I only knew that when I was well they regularly called or dropped in for coffee. Now when I needed them they did not respond. I was bitter. People were takers, not givers. They wanted my time in committees and projects. They used me to fill positions of office. Who filled my place? Who had they turned to now, to take? How had I so quickly been forgotten? Perhaps much of my bitterness was only self-pity, but I felt neglected and my family felt left out.

I cared because of Jim. He suffered his own loneliness. He could not carry on an intelligent conversation with me. I wasn't well enough to accompany him to social functions. His life revolved around the monotony of a sick wife, a demanding job, and four children and a house to keep. His entertainment consisted of reminding me constantly of my turn in cribbage. His spare time was eaten away with worry, with no recesses from his responsibilities. His conscience would not let him abandon us for a day of relaxation. He couldn't enjoy any activity knowing we were at home alone. The word *negligence* was one that haunted him even during his hours away at work. If only a couple would have dropped in—the woman to "chat" with me and (without saying so) watch the children while the man took Jim out for a round of golf. We would all have benefited from this change of routine.

I cared because of the children. They moped about the house, definitely missing the picnics and parties that had always been a part of our weekends. They were too young to control or make their own social life. They needed someone else who would make plans and provide transportation. They needed to occasionally be away from a home atmosphere that often demanded near silence or exploded into loud accusations and tears.

While I was in the hospital, June and Richard, our neighbors, took their little boy and our children to Akron to see the Christmas display of lights. Later they stopped and treated the children to doughnuts and hot chocolate. It was a comparatively inexpensive treat—one that involved, primarily, time freely given. The children still talk about that evening. If only other people would have provided other occasions.

Through my contact with the public and other patients, I realize now that people were not unfeeling—they were unsure. They did not know how to show their concern or in what form to express their help.

As I began to associate with people, I sensed their insecurity more and more. I could almost hear the questions darting about in their minds. "What do I say to her?" "What do I do?" "Should I mention her breakdown?" "Do I have to be afraid of her?" "Will she be violent?" Faced with these questions, they did what we all tend to do when confronting a strange and new situation—avoided it.

One woman admitted she was afraid that in the course of conversation she would accidentally use clichés like "What a crazy thing to say" or "You must be out of your mind." She feared what a slip of her tongue might do to me. I had to reassure her and many other people that I wasn't sensitive to these slang expressions. I was aware enough to differentiate between everyday expressions and intended accusations. The public generally assumes that if a person is having one problem he is *completely* unaware. They can't believe that a person can battle a neurosis and know his hang-ups and abilities. We've believed too long the myth that "the mentally ill are happy. They don't know any better."

To help put people at ease I coined my own nickname, "Nutty Nancy," and sometimes laughed and said, "I think I'm going out of my mind—again." Though it took much effort for me to speak of my illness flippantly, I found when we could laugh together it removed some of the tensions and discomfort.

In speaking to groups, I have discovered that lack of communication between patient and the public is the basis of most of the questions. I have visited patients and watched as their families treated them as though they were deaf and dumb. I have seen patients stop fighting because those around them consider them incapable of answering a question.

From this discussion with other patients and through my own experience, I would like to offer guidelines for visitation and also acquaint the visitor with what he can expect as he attempts to communicate with a mental patient.

First, remember that you are well and the mental patient is sick. The patient may be silent, hostile, emotional, wild-eyed, withdrawn, or slow in movement and speech. He may possibly be all of these things at some time during your visit. As he fluctuates, it is important that you remain calm, soft-spoken, and patient. You can't be allowed the privilege of resorting to accusations or furthering an emotional upheaval by argument. This is no time to defend your ego. Keep reminding yourself that you are dealing with an illogical mind, a person who cannot use "common sense."

I suggest that you accompany your visit with a small gift—a flower in a bud vase, homemade cookies, a piece of jewelry. This is a tangible expression of love, and the patient will have it to remember long after the actual visit. It also gives you an opening subject of conversation. If you wish to take reading material, choose something with colored pictures that has few words. Stay away from books that deal in subjects of controversy, illness, or religion. A "thinking of you" card is a cheerier accompaniment than a serious "get well" card.

Let the patient decide if he wants to discuss his illness. Certainly acknowledge it by saying, "I hope you are feeling better," but let him be the one to prompt any further discussion. If he does unburden himself, be a good listener. However, remember that you are not his psychiatrist or a counselor. Refrain from offering any advice, taking sides with him against his family or doctor, or disagreeing with any of his statements. Do not dismiss him with the casual remark "I understand." He will recognize this pat cliché and become antagonistic toward you. The best method is to allow him to state his feelings as you listen attentively and then tactfully lead him into a calmer topic of conversation. Any degree of anger or sympathy from you will only cause him to become more emotional.

It is important that you don't appear nervous or hurried. Never be led into the false belief that because the patient doesn't respond he isn't aware of what is happening and being said in his presence. He can be quite perceptive concerning your mood or attitude. He can sense if you are in a hurry to leave. He will also know if you fear him or are repulsed by him. Try to keep your hands quiet and speak in unhurried, soft tones.

Visiting is more successful if it is done alone. When a group visits, you are prone to carry on a lively conversation among yourselves and completely eliminate the person you have come to visit. He cannot keep up with the rapid change of topics, and the several voices will become confusing to him. As his confusion grows, the sounds will amplify inside his head until he will be overpowered and seek release in withdrawal.

Another good rule to follow: ask only questions that can be answered by fact. He can manage questions like "What did you eat for lunch?" or "Do you watch television?" Avoid questions that require an opinion. He is not ready to cope with topics like "What do you think of the student unrest?" or "Are you right with God?"

Sit quietly as you wait for the patient's answers. His thinking and his ability to articulate have been slowed down. If you watch closely, you will see signs that he is attempting to communicate. His eyes will register thought, and his mouth and hands will tell you if he is attempting to formulate an answer. For him speaking is an effort. Perhaps he thought about the answer and decided it wasn't worth the effort it would take to articulate it. Perhaps he is just stubbornly refusing to speak. Whatever the reason, if, after a reasonable length of time you notice he is not attempting to speak, go on to a different subject.

Expect outbursts of emotion. The patient is not in control. Often a gesture, a word, or one of his own thoughts will trigger angry outbursts or tears. If this happens don't become unduly upset. Don't blame yourself and overwhelm him with apologies. Don't overreact to the situation by too much sympathy or stern words of discipline. This is not a child throwing a tantrum, this is an adult under stress. Don't try to find out what is wrong. In most instances the patient will not know himself what prompted the outburst, and continued questioning to find a reason will only add to his frustration. A pat on the shoulder or a clasp of your hand will be security, and your soft voice can lead him away from his fears back onto firm ground.

Be ready to take abuse. It is often difficult to remember that those abusive retorts are originating in a sick mind. They are sometimes painfully honest and sometimes deliberately directed to your most vulnerable spot. He may accuse you of selfishness, of not loving him, of bodily cruelty. You can't resort to verbal retaliation. You can't defend yourself.

Try to forget harsh words. If you harbor resentment against the patient, *you* will be the one to suffer. The patient, when he returns to health, will probably have no recollection of unkind words. When he again expresses love for you, he won't be a hypocrite; he'll be a person once again functioning as a competent adult.

Give the patient credit for having some understanding of his condition. He is probably aware that he is very poor company. His feeling of incompetence and rejection is heightened if he finds you fidgeting and glancing repeatedly at your watch. Help him believe that your interest at that particular moment is only for him.

There is no need, though, to make the visit an endurance test for both parties. Talk brightly of topics of interest, and, before you are groping for additional conversation, stand up and leave. As you say good-by, promise another visit *only* if you mean it. He will depend on that visit, watch for your return, and, if you do not come, he will have another reason to feel rejected.

If you are close by and can call regularly, watch for signs of improvements. Don't keep him eternally ill! As he progresses and resumes some of his former activities and responsibilities, react to them. He will be proud that his behavior has improved to the point that those around him notice his accomplishments. Don't placate him with statements like, "You're almost well," or make light of his problems by saying, "Before you know it, you won't even remember you were sick." Be specific in your praise. "I'm glad to see you are reading again." He will recognize and appreciate your interest and honesty.

As you see him taking more interest in the world around him, experiment. Ask him if he would like to go for a drive, play a game, or see a movie. But abide by his decision. You aren't an authority on what's good for him. He can't be forced into new ventures, but you can give him repeated opportunities to investigate his capabilities. He won't always stay the invalid. And you can help him take those first tentative steps.

As you deal with the mental patient socially, at work, or in the neighborhood, keep in mind that 90 percent of the mentally ill are not dangerous to themselves or to other people.* There is no reason to stand at a distance as though the person is surrounded by an aura. A person recovering from an operation is welcomed back and treated normally. It is very difficult for the mental patient to return to his job if he finds that his co-workers treat him as if they expect him to have a fit at any time. It is easier to show the scar of an appendectomy than to offer proof of mental health. Make an effort to believe that his emotional scars are healing.

The best and healthiest attitude to adopt when mental illness strikes someone you love is: Be yourself. Be concerned. But be there.

During my recovery I experienced people responding in a variety of ways. Some reactions made me angry, some helped me, and some slowed my progress. As I was better able to face the world of reality, I reassured myself that the unintentional remarks and actions sprang from thoughtlessness and ignorance.

Refusal to recognize my illness was probably my biggest frustration. I had a problem. And to me the problem loomed so large that for a period of several months I was unable to think of anything else. Yet most of the people I came in contact with behaved as though there was nothing out of the ordinary. They said, "Good morning,"

---

* Edith Stern, *Mental Illness: A Guide for the Family* (New York: Harper & Row, 5th ed., 1968).

and walked quickly by. If they acknowledged my illness at all it
was to gush, "Why, there's nothing wrong with you, not Nancy?"

Why not me? I often wanted to stand up in church during the
service and shout, "Look at me. I'm mentally ill." I could find
no natural reaction. People either ignored me or turned away red-
faced and embarrassed.

I disliked having people visit me in bunches. Many weeks would
pass without a single caller; then a Sunday afternoon would come
when the living room filled with people. The house buzzed with
conversation that was seldom directed at me. The house collapsed
into disorder, children yelled, people laughed. Sound and commotion
magnified inside my head as I attempted to separate individual voices
from the multiple conversation. Yet when I excused myself to retreat
to the quiet of my own room to calm myself, I was accused of
rudeness and of being unappreciative of people's "putting themselves
out" for me.

I felt anger toward those who blindly insisted upon equating my
illness with lack of faith. Several people approached me with excited
interest and said, "What did you do that God is punishing you in
this way?" I'm sure they would have loved a whispered list of black
sins. Those who were less interested dismissed the entire problem
with the pat answer, "Pray about it and it'll all go away."

No wonder I was so grateful for Lanny, my neighbor, who talked
to me as a normal human being, showing interest in my well-being,
putting work in my hands, and smiling her praise at my small
successes!

The response to my published article was interesting. I had just
told my experience to over 8,000,000 subscribers, using my name
and the names of my husband and children; yet people were embarrassed to congratulate or even acknowledge the publication, because
they thought I would be ashamed to have it brought to my attention.
But behind me I heard conspirative whispers, "Yes, that's her. She's
the one." The freak, the odd one. Had I been foolish to admit my
illness in hopes of helping others?

Occasionally I attended our Sunday school class. I was still finding
the lessons difficult, because often I grew agitated during discussion.
One Sunday I became too upset and burst into tears. Suddenly there
was silence in the room. The leader stumbled trying to pick up

the conversation, several clustered around me asking what was wrong, others averted their eyes. Overwhelmed by my outburst, I fled the room.

About six months later the same situation presented itself. This time as I began to sob, the woman beside me, herself a former mental patient, reached over and took my hand. Quietly she kept the conversation centered on the lesson and very quickly I was in control of myself. From personal experience, Vicki knew the value of neither ignoring the person nor overreacting. She was just herself, with the additional aid of "the soft touch." I was convinced then that patients had much to share with one another.

Dr. Charles Harding, director of Harding Hospital in Worthington, Ohio, says, "The soft touch is the basis of all good therapy. I don't mean gushing expressions of sympathy that overwhelm the patient, but love and understanding accompanied by a gentle pat, or tender embrace."

When we can't think of the right words or when the situation is such that we can't speak, the soft touch is often the steadying force that helps the patient realize he is understood and loved.

I still meet people who cannot relax with me. They still keep up a wall of reserve. They are the same people who were unable to accept the diagnosis. They are the people who offered help from a safe distance. They are the people who didn't visit.

The process of recovery from mental illness is defined as growth and maturity. I hope I have grown and matured. And I hope that these people will someday overcome their fear enough to learn to know me as I am today.

Perhaps we should sympathize with these people who cannot remove the stigma from any emotional or psychiatric illness. Some day a member of their family may experience a breakdown or other form of mental disorder. Armed with only misinformation, prejudice, shame and fear, I'm sure they will especially need the companionship of friends. Then they too will wonder as I did, "Where have all the people gone?"

9

Faith and hope

Someone has said, "A breakdown is when a person stops fighting for his soul." I think an even more accurate definition would be, "A breakdown is when a person stops fighting completely."

In mental illness the loss of faith in a deity is only a portion of the patient's loss. It also includes loss of faith in people and loss of faith in himself. Much of the patient's progress will depend on changing this negative attitude into positive thinking.

The evening before my breakdown I knelt at the church altar. The large Bible was open before me and I read, "The Lord is my shepherd, I shall not want."

From the opposite page jumped the words, "My God, my God, Why hast thou forsaken me?" I began crying, and the tears blurred both scriptures.

Before my admittance to the hospital I picked up an old envelope and on the back I scrawled my own version of Psalm 23—one that portrayed my illness and depression.

> I have no one,
> And I want.
> I beg for support—
> Someone to hold my hand.
> This way leads through mire, past gutters
> swirling in slime and soiled slush.
> I am an empty useless vessel.

No one comes here but me. And so the way is
   dark and unexplored.
I fumble for footholds, through a chasm
   steep and uncharted. I cannot see through
   the mist and there is no end. The years have
   eroded an infinite gorge.
Would that I have with me
   light, love or learning.
But before me are only hostile eyes of suspicion,
   judgment and rejection.
I have nothing to combat them,
   for my resistance, like an earthen jar,
   lies shattered at their feet.
There is no mercy but death.
And death is not readily bestowed.
So I shall wander upon this land
   alone, forever.
            So be it.

Death appeared more alluring than life. I, like millions of other people, was wanting to escape from a life of desolation of mind and spirit.

Later, as I lay on my hospital bed, I wondered why, when I had been in church since an infant and called myself Christian for as long as I could remember, I felt no communication with God. Supposedly I had been preparing for just such an emergency as this, by training myself to have confidence in a heavenly father. Why, then, did I feel nothing? There wasn't even a void where my spiritual faith had been. I had no desire to formulate even a sentence prayer. In fact, my interest in the subject was so small that I can't recall investigating it any further. Reality, for me, at that time, was the first two lines of my psalm parody, "I have no one/And I want."

In retrospect I am able to see the logical loss and return of faith and hope. At the time I was living it, I wasn't able to discuss or even concern myself with religious matters. First had to come the battle to understand and accept myself. Then I had to reestablish human relations. Last was to come my reacquaintance, or, perhaps I should say, my *discovery* of God.

Through reading case histories and the assurance of other people,

I was led to expect that this progression would take place. I discovered that it could not be hurried and that its accomplishment would require a great deal of determination. My battle of the spirit has taken the longest, but I believe it has wrought the greatest change in me.

One day in the hospital, as I lay on my bed, the nurse brought me a floral arrangement. "Nancy, sit up. Look at the flowers I've brought you."

I turned on my side away from her. "I don't want to see them. I'm tired. Let me alone."

"Of course you want to see them. They are carnations made to look like a strawberry soda. Even straws and an artificial cherry. It's from Elaine. Is she a friend?"

Admitting to a friendship would have been becoming more involved with the nurse than I was ready to be, so I only admitted grudgingly, "I know her."

When I didn't turn to accept the flowers, the nurse placed them on my table and said, "Well, I want you to comb your hair. It'll soon be visiting hours and you'll want to look nice for your husband."

"I'm not going to comb my hair. No one cares what I look like."

She sighed and straightened my pillow. She left the room, going on to other patients, probably, I thought, hoping to find one more cooperative.

When I was alone I crawled out of bed and walked to the window. Four stories down I saw Lilliputian people hurrying up and down the sidewalks. What could send them scurrying so fast? How foolish they were to strive for accomplishments. "Hey, stupid people, don't you know there is no purpose to life? No reason to plan a future? No reason to comb your hair?"

I turned back and looked at my sterile room. My world was here. A limbo world that was as fragile as mist but as suffocating as smoke. A place of distortions—people out of focus, thoughts defying logic. There were no foundation and no facts here. Life had shattered and the spider-webbed fragments were too intricate to reassemble into a pattern. I crawled back into bed and covered my face with my arm.

Later a nurse's aide brought the mail. After she had gone, I sat on the edge of the bed and opened the stack of cards. I ignored

the printed verses of cheer and only rapidly glanced at the names
of the senders and their short messages.

Ginny, the widow caring for the children, wrote, "Don't worry
about your family. I'm available when needed." I dropped the card.
Why would I worry about them? I seldom even thought about them.
They had stayed behind in the world of hurrying people. They didn't
know about this strange world where I had gone.

"Many love and need you. Get well, dear one." Signed, Mary.
Those words angered me. No one loved me. No one needed me.
Why did she tell foolish lies like that?

"From one who has walked in that particular place. My thoughts
are with you." . . . Doris. I reread that one. Maybe she knew about
the gorge and the mist. I laid her card aside.

I threw the cards into a drawer, turned over in bed, and pulled
the sheet high over my head. I was tired of reading.

In a few minutes I reached out and picked up the card from
Doris, and pulled it under the sheet with me. It crackled against
my cheek. "From one who has walked in that particular place . . ."

Once the no-visitor ban had been lifted, Jim came every afternoon
and evening to see me. He entered the room with a spring in his
step, a smile, and subjects for conversation. His energy exhausted
me. I didn't even want to return the smile. Only now do I realize
the effort it cost him to present that picture of hope and enthusiasm.

He talked about people, his job, the children. He told me about
the people who asked about me, what the doctor had reported. Words
. . . words . . . words. So many of them. And I couldn't concentrate
long enough to remember even a sentence.

I didn't answer him. I gritted my teeth and clenched my fists
trying to make sense of what he was saying. Beyond that, everything
else was impossible. "Don't worry," he kept saying.

Don't worry . . . worry . . . worry. About who . . . who . . .
who? I am dying, don't you know that? It's the only way out
of this foggy, confusing world that swirls and muddles everything.
Leave me . . . leave . . . leave me. Don't make me struggle.

But when Jim had gone, he took with him the remnants of that
real world, and the sound of his voice. Alone I cried against the
silence and against the isolation of my mind.

Every morning Jim called the hospital to ask if I needed anything. During my stay I asked for a variety of things—music, make-up, clean gowns. Some time during the morning he would make a special trip to the hospital to deliver them. One morning I was talking to a group of patients and was angry at the nurse for interrupting my conversation when she said, "Your husband wants to know if you have a message for him."

Imitating a Hollywood screen star, I mocked, "Tell him 'I love you.' "

We all laughed except the nurse. She left the room.

I forgot about the joke until Jim came to visit me. He held my hands and with a choked voice said, "Thank you for your message."

Message? What message, I thought?

"I love you, too."

That, I thought? I said that to be funny. But looking at his gentle face, I didn't tell him.

My message had been bitten with sarcasm, but the nurse had delivered it in a tone of love. Jim had heard the words, and that was all. I thought about it. What had begun as a joke for my fellow patients had turned into a meaningful communication with my husband. I drew back, frightened by this hint of giving.

As I spent more time outside my room, I grew more interested in these people with whom I lived. I learned of their problems. I learned that they also felt lonely and estranged from their families and the world of reality. They understood this limbo world of the mist. But we were not in this other world together; we each inhabited our own world of isolation. We sometimes came together through mutual understanding and suffering, but we each withdrew into our chambers of fear when decisions came too close.

Because as patients we understood one another, we found it much easier to talk to each other than to anyone else. We gave and accepted help among ourselves that we would have resisted if offered by an outsider, even our doctor. We were alike, and yet we were each in isolation.

With this giving and taking came experimenting. I combed my hair, not because I was told to do it, but because the other patients were doing it and I was a part of their society. Conversation with them made the hour I spent with Jim easier. I was less afraid of talking. By concentrating I could manage an interest in the events taking place outside of the hospital. One day I heard a joke and remembered it until visiting hours. I was glad it made Jim laugh. I was pleased that I had contributed to the visit, rather than just brusquely answering the questions put to me.

I still resented the staff. The nurses and the doctor seemed to be administrators of punishment. They issued orders like, "Take your bath," "Eat your meals," "Don't lie on your bed," "Swallow your pills." When you disobeyed, they wrote something on their mysterious charts. The nurses "tattled" to the doctor. At times the atmosphere was strained as the patients silently lined up against the staff. We revolted in subtle ways. A game deliberately pushed onto the floor. Coffee spilled across the food on the tray. Capsules held in our mouths and then spit down the toilet and flushed away. Fighting back against suggested cooperation.

As time went by I noticed acts of kindness on the part of the staff. How silently they took our rebuffs. How quietly they always spoke. How patiently they repeated suggestions, waiting for a positive response. They personified discipline. I eventually was able to recognize their roles. They were not baby-sitters hired to mollycoddle us, but professionals trained to restore us to a productive life.

I know I had made progress when I was able to feel respect for these people. I recalled my Twenty-third Psalm and knew that life was not the negative passion I had written. I asked the nurse for paper and pencil. This dawning of reaching out and responding to people had burned away part of the mist and I wrote:

> I have many friends
>> Who want to help.
> They support me on either side
>> As I tremble in my first steps.
> They give me a bed to lie upon in peace.
> Though the treatments stretch before me darkly
>> And I pass through minutes of oblivion
> I know on the other side they await to
>> minister to me.
> They bring with them their talent, their love and concern.
>> And it is good.
> I can ask for no better care.

Surely with such support I will arrive wholly well
Surely . . .
Surely . . .

The seed of hope and faith was planted. How would it be nurtured?

I was dismissed from the hospital and, as was true in other areas, I also regressed spiritually. In the controlled atmosphere of the hospital, complete health had seemed feasible and I had been inspired to work toward it. At home, healing of any kind seemed an impossibility. I felt distrust and disgust with myself, my family, and my doctor. I had no self-confidence, and I mistrusted the efforts of others. This inability to cope with the outside world confirmed my belief that I was worthless.

I went back to the beginning and started building a self-image and involving myself in interpersonal relationships. Somewhere between this ugliness of failure and the idealism of the girl in the flowered dress there had to be a workable philosophy.

During my search I was hindered, angered, and frustrated by people offering advice and platitudes. Too many "good" people felt they had the immediate cure-all for my illness. Like Cinderella's godmother, they felt they possessed the magic wand that changed circumstances in the flippant wave of a cliché. "Just pray about it and it'll go away." "What did you do that God is punishing you this way?" "Have faith." My instinctive reaction was to want to scream back at them, but I knew I wasn't allowed that privilege. If I had fought back, they would have been convinced I was crazy and would have gone away piously shaking their heads over my demented soul. As much as I resented their piety, I had to control my temper and remain silent.

Recently I picked up a religious publication and read an article whose theme was, "How can a Christian have a breakdown when he walks with God and has constant peace of mind?"

One of the new concepts of mental breakdowns is that the patient is involved in a high stress situation. Find the person or circumstance responsible for this tension, remove it, and you have begun to help the patient. If this is true, are we saying that Christians are immune to high stress situations? What about military combat? Financial disaster? A child killed on the highway? An unhappy marriage? That a Christian moves in a protective capsule is another myth. A breakdown is a mental safety valve that comes to our rescue and temporarily releases us from circumstances too horrible or difficult to confront immediately. Rather than berating a person for having too little faith, why can't we see this as God's way of saying, "Rest, my child, until you are well enough once again to pick up your burden." I can see no basis for judging an individual as having too little faith and thus adding to his guilt.

Now that I am progressing I am willing to admit that the majority of these people who offer their verbal quack remedies believe they are offering words of comfort. But remembering my own difficult time and hearing other patients describe to me oral tortures meted out by people, I remember Jesus' words, "Father, forgive them, for they know not what they do." But as yet the words are said in bitterness and with mockery. Perhaps it will be quite some time before I can say them with compassion.

Attending church is difficult for any patient. I'm just lately beginning to derive peace from worship, rather than turmoil.

One evening I attended a silent meditation. As I was coming out of the church, a woman stopped me. "Nancy! How good to see you. How are you?"

I was particularly discouraged and was grateful for this opening of interest and concern. "Not very well," I said. "It's taking a long time."

She took my hand. "Have you prayed about it?"

I had tried to explain this phase of mental illness to other people and knew how futile it was to make them understand in a few sentences. It would be useless to tell her that for many months my prayers had died without hope even before they took form in my thoughts. She would have seen only the failure on my part.

She went on. "You know, don't you, all you need is faith and you'll be well."

What a quick summation, I thought.

I tried to smile as I answered, "The doctor believes I *am* sick. He believes the remedy is more than the need to recite a prayer." I felt myself getting angry. How could she pronounce judgment without knowing the probing that the doctor and I were doing into the dark, unexplored portions of my mind? How could she, without knowing how much we hoped to tap strength that had thus far been dormant? I felt like a trapped, bound cocoon. She was offering the metamorphosis of magic, when I knew it took the same meticulous scientific order that would be involved in a caterpillar's emerging as a butterfly. Neither transformation was going to come about without a proper order and progression.

She stood there chattering about her "blue days." She assured me that even she was discontent to the point of tears. She continued to pat my arm. "You're just depressed. Get down on your knees and you'll find your worries disappear. If you love God enough, he'll make you well."

I tightened and pulled away from her touch. *Just* depressed! How glibly she shook off my hellish prison. *Just* depressed.

Hoping to control my anger, I answered in a monotone. "It's not that easy."

"Of course, it's that easy. I have some books I'll bring you. You'll see. After you read them, you'll wonder where you ever got this foolish idea of being ill."

I broke away from her and drove home, but her words had planted their doubt. As I lay in bed that night trying to calm myself enough to fall asleep, I began to wonder, "Is it all imaginary? I don't want to be this way. I want to be like other people, not smothered in indecision and doubt, crying for hours for some unknown reason."

The words from the Bible came back to me. "Why hast thou forsaken me?" I wasn't just asking God, I was questioning people and my own logical sense.

At my next therapy session I cried out my doubts to the doctor. He snapped the pencil he was toying with, got up, and paced the floor.

"So someone got to you. These people and their misdirected guidance! There is no connection between your religion and mental illness. Why will people run to a surgeon with a gall bladder attack and still believe that mental illness is imaginary? A person in depression has enough uncertainties to cope with, without someone insinuating that he is sick because he hasn't prayed hard enough. How can they add to a person's misery by making him believe even God won't give his love to them? Why make them doubt themselves even more?"

"Listen to me, Nancy, mental illness is not a punishment! It is not imaginary! And it is nothing to be ashamed of!" He ran his hands through his black hair. "Two women who experienced breakdowns about the time you did have deteriorated into permanent deficiency because their families have hidden them away in shame and refused to provide them with an atmosphere of love and understanding. Of the thirty-five people hospitalized with you, one has been committed to a state institution and thirty-four have experienced various degrees of progress. No, we don't know all there is to know about the human mind, but we can help people when they recognize their need and come to us."

He dropped back into his chair. "Excuse me, but I get plain mad when I hear about people like that. They are the same ones who are denied visitation rights because they have been caught pointing their finger at a patient and quoting in a voice of doom, 'All have sinned and come short of the glory of God.' When will they learn to help their loved ones by praying *for* them in private, rather than distressing them by praying *with* them?"

His agitation had surprised me, but I was relieved that his response was so emotional. It substantiated my own rebellious feelings.

As I was leaving that day, he looked kindly into my eyes. "Yes, Nancy, you are sick, but I'm going to help you get well."

After that assurance, whenever I encountered a person bent on equating mental illness with religion, I excused myself and fled from the possible argument.

It wasn't until I entered my second year of recovery that I began my own search for faith and a workable philosophy for my life. By this time the doctor and I had completely talked out my false conception of the world and I had made some progress in accepting myself as a human being with abilities and failures. I already knew that there wasn't a line drawn between sickness and health. Mental health was growth. The doctor was not just solving my current set of problems, he was also equipping me to have the insight to meet and solve future problems.

Now, I naively thought, I am ready to pursue my loss of faith in God. Every phase of my recovery had taken time, yet my conservative upbringing still made me think that my faith in God would return in a burst of light. I would receive a revelation.

Since I was impatient I would hurry the miracle. I turned on the radio to the local religious radio station. I would assimilate faith while I did housework. One day, as I dusted to the beat of "When the Saints Go Marching In," I realized how foolish I was. I was not going to absorb beliefs through repetitive gospel rhythms or evangelistic haranguing.

Next I tried the religious book section of the library. I skipped over the books on history and denominations. I read a few autobiographies. The authors assured me over and over that during the crisis of illness, famine, or flood, God walked with them hand in hand. I rather doubted such slick religion. Surely they too had felt lost and alone sometimes. I just wasn't convinced they were being honest. Since I doubted part of their story, I wasn't sure that I could believe any of it.

Next I turned to spiritual life books. Their themes were soothing. They talked a lot about nature and peace and perfection, but to me they smacked too much of the girl in the flowered dress. I got the idea they were sugar-coating reality.

Finally I came to the current revolutionists. They challenged me with interesting questions. They used words like "nitty-gritty" and "gut-level." They dwelled on our past failures. I was interested in what they had to say, but when I finished their books they still hadn't given me any answers. They afflicted me without then giving me any comfort. Soon their complaints became repetitious and I became bored.

I had reached the end of the bookshelf, knowing the style and technique of many writers but no nearer to rediscovering faith.

About this time an editor wrote me a letter. He said, in part: "I'm glad that you were free to mention your recent breakdown. Experiences like that lose their fear for us when we face them freely and admit them to others. I am sure that you have learned through the experience and that you know God better for it, and I feel closer to you for your having told me. My own breakdown, a number of years ago, was a tremendous growing experience."

I sat with the letter in my hand and an empty feeling inside me. Would I know God better for this? Would I grow? At this point in my search, I felt just the opposite. God would ever evade me. Nothing would ever come to give me confidence or hope to believe in a future.

My thoughts went back to the hospital. How could such a society work? How could there be harmony there and a climate conducive to healing? And I remembered we were people in trouble administering to people in trouble.

Then I questioned myself. What had my religion meant to me so far? As a child I had learned the "don'ts" of Christianity. Don't smoke, don't drink, don't swear. Be cooperative and obedient, and don't question the Sunday school teacher or the preacher. This was supposed to be the simple formula of a happy life and an eternal reward. But I listened to the Ladies Aid maliciously gossiping about another person. I saw migrant families living in filth along the road we used to drive to church. I was warned never to speak to the black men living at the railroad camp. I was supposed to be nice to the "poor" children in school, but I wasn't to play with them, they might have lice.

Later church was to feed my ego. It served as a platform for my talents. I had only to be neat and clean, sing clearly, play the piano sweetly, and teach an uncontroversial lesson to be looked upon as a "good Christian." I was adept at smiling and hiding my feelings, so it wasn't difficult to perform in this play-acting. I had no time to worry about the filth of the migrants or the lice of the poor; I was too busy planning next year's missionary program.

I attended many churches after my marriage as we moved from place to place. A little adobe church that specialized in spaghetti suppers and gospel singing. A very rich church where the people met all of the needs of the church with a personal check—new carpeting, new lighting, a new organ. There was a church of ambitious young people where Sunday school class was a congenial hour, and everyone's social life involved everyone else. A very tightly knit group.

Evidently my religion meant attending meetings in the nearest church of my denomination. I guess my experience could best be described as "self-satisfying." My association with the church made me feel "good." Sunday school class seemed to be a weekly opportunity to sit with other people and share our "good" deeds of the past week. We spent the time convincing each other that our prejudices, apathy, and lack of involvement were justified because of our work, our families, and our times. Of what benefit, though, was salving our conscience each Sunday to go back into the world and live as selfishly as we had the week before?

The question I finally had to ask myself was how much of my religion had been for the glorification of Nancy and how much of it had been for the glorification of God?

It seemed God's name and Jesus' philosophy were noticeably missing from my past experience!

Again I thought back to the hospital. What *had* been there to make it a climate for healing? Honesty . . . love . . . time to communicate with individuals . . . people caring for people . . . no one judged by his language, his smoking, his hair length, his race, his financial status. Was it even possible to find that kind of relationship away from the hospital?

So far the only progress I had seemed to make was that I had lost my smugness. I was willing to admit that I didn't want to regain my religion, but I wanted to discover God. I heard a minister say, "Some of the most neurotic people I know are religious people trying to be Christian." Could I push over the dogma of my past and learn to be Christian? Gratification was not enough. I wanted peace.

That spring I discovered the foundation. I knelt one day and cradled a pansy flower in my palm. There in the garden with the sun warm on my back and the smell of moist dirt, I looked into the perfection of that one flower. Its round yellow center seemed to be a tiny mouth formed in an O of surprise at my attention. It seemed to be afraid of my hands. I held it gently and reassured it, "Anything as exquisite as you had to be made by God." I looked about me at the other flowers, the trees, the clouds, the birds. "There is a God. This I'm sure of."

One fact . . . one admission. Then I was not alone. I had not been alone in my world of the mist and I was not alone as I struggled to find faith. "You are God and I believe in You. You are the prime mover, the life in the atom, the face of the pansy, the ruler of the universe, the one who can and will quiet my soul and dissolve the loneliness."

But how?

How far did my awareness of life extend? It was respect for all living things that made me notice the pansy. It was my recognition of the compassion of other people that made me often wish to return to the hospital and its haven of understanding. Above all, I was thankful for each day and the ability to function in it. I was appreciative of health. I began searching for these qualities in other people.

But people seemed to move about from work to recreation and leisure in isolation, avoiding direct glances, physical touch, and verbal communication. The larger the crowd, the more isolated the individual seemed to be. The conversation held them apart by its trivia.

I remembered a man once saying in a Sunday school class, "Would you all still treat me as a friend if I were charged with embezzling?" The class assured him they would. He had retorted bitterly, "I don't believe you. Let any of us veer from the norm and he would be closed out of the group."

Now as I searched for compassion and communication I began to agree with the man. We appear to want a society of mediocrity, no one too smart, no one too dumb, too rich, too poor. Conformity breeds anonymity. And people evidently prefer anonymity or they are afraid to voice their needs and fears.

A man and a woman in a small church were discovered having a love affair. It was twenty years before an automobile accident finally freed the man from the accusing tongues and eyes of the congregation. If this is the way man treats man, perhaps we are wise to present a veneer to safeguard ourselves from abuse.

Yet many of the people, including myself, who had been hospitalized were there because we led two lives, the one of loneliness, fear, and failure and the other the bright smiling exterior for the world to see.

My search came at the same time as the wave of movies on homosexuality. Because of these Hollywood stories, society was suspicious of all deep personal relationships. We looked askance on a close friendship between two men, two women, or a man and a woman other than mates. Because of these taboos our interpersonal relationships had been reduced to *using* one another rather than *knowing* one another.

Did I have to forget about the honesty of the hospital and put back my mask and once again function in a world of people who didn't touch one another's lives? And if I did, how long would it be before I found myself once again in mental and emotional trouble?

I turned to my children. They had shown more love and forgiveness during my illness than any adult. Since I still wasn't strong enough to cope with a wide circle of friends, I could be selective. My closeness with the children proved to be spiritually building. They were too young to be insincere. They still loved with exuberance and got angry with volume. And they openly expressed their revelations. One morning as we sat on the floor in our pajamas sharing a pot of tea, Craig said, "People nice on the inside are always beautiful outside, no matter how they look." Because Craig is loving, he sees beauty in many people. I needed to learn how to be beautiful inside and discover beauty in the people around me.

I saw my associates differently now. Before I was quick to condemn and ridicule. Now I ask myself, "Why did that individual act in the way he did?" I soon discovered that where I covered up my insecurities by wanting to be best (the big frog in a little pond) other people had other methods of hiding: anger, snobbishness, pretended ailments, gossip. As it became easier to understand the person, I soon found I was no longer aware of his mask. I saw the person behind the façade.

I wanted to communicate with God, but how should I begin? It's always difficult speaking the first time to someone you have ignored for a considerable length of time. My first prayer was short. "Thank you for giving me today. I now give it back to you. Please return it to me an hour at a time with the ability to live that hour to its fullest." I continued using it as my morning prayer.

I went to the Bible for reassurance. Joshua 1:9 said, "Be strong and of a good courage; be not afraid, neither be thou dismayed: for the Lord Thy God is with thee whithersoever thou goest."

As I felt the stirrings of an inner peace and the ability to relate to people, I knew that God had not forsaken me. He had been present, but the failure to recognize his presence had been part of my illness. These words from Joshua spoken to my healthy mind were a comfort. Those same words spoken to me earlier would have been abrasives dragged across a wounded mind. I understood even more why it was important not to dwell on religion with a mental patient. My mind had healed enough that I was picking up my own fight for my soul, and that was as it should be.

The words of the editor were beginning to come true for me. I was beginning to know myself and other people better for this experience. And now at last I was beginning to feel that I also knew God better for it.

Later that summer a man approached me one morning after an outdoor worship service and said, "Don't you believe in miracles in regard to mental illness?"

"Yes," I said, "I lived one."

He waved my words away with impatience. "No, I don't mean that kind. I mean healing in an instant. I go into mental hospitals, lay my hands on a person's head, and heal him instantly."

If that is true, I thought, then several million people would appreciate your calling on them during visiting hours.

But I said, "I don't deny the possibility of *any* healing taking place in an instant. We have the Scriptures' description of these miracles, but I do not encourage families to idly wait for this type of healing to come their way. My respect goes to the families who are living 'hard-worked-for miracles.' And these miracles are being accomplished because of the knowledge and dedication of nurses and doctors, and the love and understanding of lay people. When I was unable to receive God's love directly, I now know that he ministered to me through people who were willing to be instruments of his power. And that, sir, to me, is a miracle of a great deal of love."

As I see parents with emotionally disturbed children attending seminars to learn more about mental illness to better help that child, or as I talk to a woman who for twenty-six years has transported her husband to doctors to try to dispel the horrors of Stalag 17, it proves to me that *instant* miracles are the "easy kind." Any of us would hold a possessed person in our arms and instantly heal him if we had the power. The results would be quick and we would be heralded as heroes. But how many of us would lovingly devote twenty-six years and longer to the daily, trying task of living with a mentally disturbed person? To me the hard-worked-for miracles are more characteristic of Christ's love than is divine magic. 1 John 4:12 says, "No one has ever seen God; but as long as we love one another God will live in us and his love will be complete in us" (*The Jerusalem Bible*).

Since I wasn't too strong yet, I returned to FISH, an ecumenical organization of Christians working together to provide emergency

help to others. FISH's work is all volunteer, and I could give my
time as I felt able. It could be providing transportation, caring for
children, providing food or clothing, helping those who are sick.
Its one-line creed, "Christ loves you and so do I," seemed to be
just another way of saying 1 John 4:12. This, after all my searching,
best illustrated what I felt religion was about.

One day, while I was ironing, the phone rang. It was Irene, a
fellow FISH worker. "Nancy, could you help someone? Her name
is Edna. She has mental problems. Several of us have tried talking
to her, but we can't seem to reach her. Knowing you've been there,
we thought maybe you would know the proper thing to say or do
to let her know we want to help."

With much apprehension I said yes. After I hung up the receiver,
I leaned against the wall. All of these feelings were still very close
to me. Would I be able to be strong enough to help her, or would
I identify too much with her and experience a setback myself?

As I crawled into the car, I remembered one of FISH's rules
and I prayed. "I'm going out in Your name to one of Your people.
Help me."

Irene met me at the door. Behind her stood Edna, hair tangled,
eyes wild, face swollen from crying, her hands twisting a damp
handkerchief. She could have been me or any one of my friends
from the hospital.

She screamed at me, "I'll give you fifteen minutes to make me
well and then you get out of my house."

Irene whispered to me. "Are you all right?"

I nodded.

Irene left the house and we were alone.

I found out Edna was a recent widow. She had three young children
and a mother who did not recognize mental illness as a legitimate
reason for not being able to function. Overwhelmed by decisions
she had never before had to make and grieving for a husband who
had died instantly of a heart attack, she had tried to escape through
suicide.

When she discovered I understood the emotional upheaval she
was now experiencing, she began talking. But she did continue to
remind me that I didn't know exactly how she felt, because I had
not lost my husband. I had no intention of arguing with her. None
of us know the problems of another, or an individual's endurance

level. We have no right to judge another's breaking point. But I did understand depression, fear, and indecision. I could talk to her.

We did talk for two and a half hours. I constantly came back to the statement, "I will listen to you, Edna, but I can't solve your problems. You need professional help." She was already receiving too much amateur advice, and each person's opinion added to her confusion.

I gave her my doctor's name and tried to persuade her to call him. "No," she said, "I'm not crazy. I don't need a head-shrinker. It's too expensive."

Her mother entered the room in time to voice her opinion in broken English. "Edna, she not sick. You want to know about sick, ask me. I know what means to be sick. Every week I go to doctor for medicine."

"Your sickness is physical and every week you seek help from the person qualified to help you. Why won't you convince your daughter to go to the doctor who can help her?"

I stood up to leave. "If you don't want help, there is no use of my staying any longer."

Edna ran to me and gripped my head between her hands, pressing until my head ached. "Were you like me? Tell me, were you?"

"Yes," I assured her.

"But your eyes are bright; you smiled at me. Let me inside of you. I don't want to be me. I want to be you."

I put my arms around her and held her as she cried.

"Help me. Please help me. Perform a miracle and make me well."

A miracle again! I thought of my own hard struggle. I wished she did not have to travel that same road, but I also knew there was no other way. And the sooner she began the journey, the shorter the route would be. I urged her again, "Call my doctor."

The following Saturday, Edna was grabbed just as she tried to lunge through a fourth story window downtown. An ambulance was called. On her way to the hospital she murmured my name and my doctor's name over and over.

The doctor knew when he heard my name how she had known to ask for him. He injected a sedative into her arm. Edna was already receiving her help, but her cry had almost been fatal.

When I found out she was in the hospital, I remembered her

burying her head in my shoulder and saying, "I want to be like you."

How many others besides Edna wanted to have bright eyes and a smiling face? How many other minds had escaped this world and were now wandering in the dark lonely chasm of mist as convinced as I had been that they had no one, that the way was dark and unexplored and no one went there but them?

But in what way was I qualified to touch another life? What did I really know about mental illness? Would I know the right thing to say? What if I answered a call and the person was violent? It was the old Nancy asking these questions, trying to escape responsibility. What had happened to my new belief in 1 John 4:12? Was I going to accept it as a testimony of faith or was I going to twist it into a complex theological thesis?

A Negro made the statement about racism: "I derive enough love from Christ that people don't have to love me back." This was the type of faith I wanted. I wanted the communication between God and me to be open so that I no longer had to cling to people, begging for praise and acceptance. I didn't want to say "I love you" to a person because I needed that person to say "I love you" in return. I wanted to receive my strength from God and pass it on to anyone who might need encouragement or the "soft touch."

An editor said to me, "Are you ready to be identified with mental illness?"

Was I? I knew there would be other phone calls, other Ednas asking for help.

I jotted down on a piece of paper my new definition of faith.

Faith is: 1. Compatibility of the conscious and unconscious man.
             2. Rewarding interpersonal relationships.
             3. Communication with God.

I remembered Doris's card, "From one who has walked in that particular place. My thoughts are with you." Her words had helped me. Didn't I have to help someone else?

Through Edna had I at last found a meaning for my life? I was frightened, but I prayed, "Thank you, God, for giving me the experience of a breakdown to say to other people like me, I understand. If this is where I can be of service, use me."

With this commitment I dispelled the last of my morose version of the Twenty-third Psalm and was able to appreciate the words of comfort . . .

> The Lord is my shepherd; I shall not want.
> He maketh me to lie down in green pastures: he leadeth me beside the still waters.
> He restoreth my soul: he leadeth me in the paths of righteousness for his name's sake.
> Yea, though I walk through the valley of the shadow of death, I will fear no evil: for thou art with me; thy rod and thy staff they comfort me.
> Thou preparest a table before me in the presence of mine enemies: thou anointest my head with oil; my cup runneth over.
> Surely goodness and mercy shall follow me all the days of my life: and I will dwell in the house of the Lord forever.
>
> *Amen.*

10

Coming back

I understand how young people feel when they have majored in a certain field, completed their education, and then been told they can't have a job until they've proven themselves.

After spending two years in psychoanalysis, fighting my fears, forming a new self-image, and developing a workable philosophy, I felt ready to reestablish my place in society. But when I tried to step back into the mainstream of living, I found my place was no longer there. My attempts were like standing on the shore of a quiet lake and tossing a pebble into its depths. The water swallows the stone, quivers slightly, then ignores the minute intrusion. I had been plucked from a busy life, restored to health, and set back in the world, but I was now a stranger. Moving about was like awakening into "The Twilight Zone." I knew all the characters but they only responded to me in the polite greetings of strangers. My efforts were no more than minute intrusions.

Returning to society is the last great problem the patient will face in his recovery. It is a very real struggle, but it is a problem that shouldn't even exist.

It took me quite awhile to realize there wasn't going to be any welcoming committee. I had, instead, moved into what has long been known in mental health as the "semantic jail." The public has an image of the mentally ill. They have established names and descriptions for people who have emotional problems. They have preconceived ideas of how patients behave. Before me was a wall of "labels." No one was eager to have me back. If I wanted to return to a full life, I would have to fight for a place in it. It was perfectly clear that I was to be considered guilty of incompetence, subject to explosions of emotions (perhaps violence) and erratic behavior—all of which were polite terms for "queer," "odd," "crazy," "insane." Society, the stone-faced jury, confronted me and demanded, "Prove your sanity." But even as I presented my case, they closed their minds or proved to be too busy to listen.

Labels tend to lock persons in roles, sometimes permanently. If a patient is told repeatedly, "You can't," he will eventually believe it and live out his life as a totally dependent person. The patient has expectations, but they can be altered or even destroyed by his interpersonal relationships. This is why the patient's family and friends need to be especially educated and alert to the patient's needs and abilities during this final stage. Ignorance during this time can undo all of the tedious work that has gone before. If people shy away from contact with the patient, he will soon feel rejected. Unable to communicate with people, he will escape back into his fantasy world. The person who is deprived of tasks of responsibility will see himself as incompetent and lose even the basic skills like dressing himself.

It is cruel that the fighting has to be done by the person who is convalescing. This is a time of unsureness, a time when the self-image is still weak, when the ability to rely on self-judgment is at its lowest. No wonder the patient is often too tired to establish a place for himself, that he eventually accepts the role society has cast him in, and plays out his life, helpless to change it.

I heard around me people singing:

> O brother man, fold to thy heart thy brother;
> Where pity dwells, the peace of God is there;
> To worship rightly is to love each other,
> Each smile a hymn, each kindly deed a prayer.*

But they sang their hymn of compassion with their backs turned!

I began attending meetings of the groups I had participated in

*John Greenleaf Whittier.

before my illness. I believed my attendance proved that I was interested in the organization. The Writer's Guild welcomed me back, eagerly read my manuscripts, and helped me relearn my writing style. At the next election they elected me secretary, and I performed my duties on time and correctly. With their help I was able to face realistically the rejection of some of the other groups.

When I was not accepted by some people, I got up enough courage to volunteer for committees. The answer was always the same, "Thank you, we'll call you if we need you." The phone never rang. I grew ashamed of not being wanted.

Eventually this brought me to a difficult decision. Even though certain people had once been important to me as friends and associates, when they could not accept first my illness and now my recovery, I had to sever connection with them and develop new interests and friends. Because I was fortunate enough to have some people accept me, I didn't feel compelled to prove to all people that I was competent in order to have faith in myself.

I was fortunate. I knew by my mail that many people had been rebuffed until they had isolated themselves and were living their lives as recluses. I understood their hiding behind drawn blinds. Many times as I tried to "fit in" I was tempted to quit, but the doctor explained to me that every person needs ways of contributing to feel worthwhile, and I kept trying.

Again, to be fair, I had to think that perhaps the public didn't know the importance of their reaction to the returning patient.

First, the patient needs to feel welcome in his own home and neighborhood. It is true that others have had to assume his responsibilities for months or even years, but they must willingly step down now and give the patient the opportunity to prove himself. A father must have the chance of eventually resuming being the head of the house. The mother will have to manage her household and rear her children.

Small, "busy" jobs are not enough. A man who once earned $20,000 a year will not feel he is carrying his share of the load by taking out the garbage. He may begin with easy household tasks, but don't hold him there and don't praise him for this simple job by gushing, "Good boy," as if he were a well-trained dog.

If the patient takes more time than usual to complete a job, or does not do it as well as you could yourself, don't damage his confidence by interfering. Constantly interrupted by impatient words and gestures, he will cease to try.

Be careful of the attitude you convey when suggesting activities. He is going to rebel against the "it's good for you" attitude as surely as any child. Don't arrange his life with *your* idea of what he needs. The alert family and friends will watch carefully for the patient to reveal his own interests and capabilities. Guide him in those interests.

As he is ready for social functions, let him do the choosing. He will be the only one who can determine what helps him and what hinders him. No one else can know what upsets him and what gives him comfort or gratification. Don't plan a dinner party because you enjoy conversation and therefore assume it will be stimulating for the patient. For him, a quiet trip to the library may be a meaningful step towards rehabilitation.

Use good judgment in reacting to his accomplishments. If he is ignored, he will feel rejected, but if you are overenthusiastic, he will be insulted and angered. He deserves a deeper response than a pat on the head. Guard against the foolish conversation children have to suffer. Don't talk too loudly, too clearly, or in a simplified vocabulary. The patient, rather than being lifted by this false cheer, is repulsed.

Association with former patients and their families is usually a good starting place for social functions. The patient will be more relaxed with those who understand what he is going through, and he will be more likely to attempt something new, knowing that if he fails he is with people who will not fasten a label on him. With these people he doesn't have to weigh each answer and movement to decide how it will be received. At first his emotions will not be in control, and he will burst into tears or explosions of anger when he becomes frustrated. Former patients will not add to his embarrassment by withdrawing in shock. They can help him by being there and laying a calming hand on his.

I learned, as others have, not to indulge in spontaneous reactions in public. Other people may react violently or hysterically and be accepted, but this is a luxury too expensive for the mental patient. Whenever he responds in excess, it can be interpreted as a "fit."

No more could I pound my golf club when I dropped into a sand trap, argue loud and long for my point in a discussion, or sob in a sad movie. This was like raising a flag for people to nod their heads and reaffirm, "She has mental problems—beware!" I learned to practice moderation in all emotions—another type of jail. At home my family was the sounding board for my pent-up frustrations.

As time has passed, I have gained confidence in myself and been able to find humor in people's childish reactions. There are times when I have known I could panic a group by waving my arms and making strange noises. They are so plainly frightened by mental illness. Often as I stand in front of a group to speak, I see fear in their eyes, in their fluttering hands, or in their inability to look at me. This is part of my challenge, to win them over to me as a person and as a patient, so they are relaxed enough to ask their questions at the end of my talk. It is more sad than funny that ignorance is still holding people in terror of the emotionally ill.

Often it is important to know what has made the person "break." Some doctors are now looking outside the individual to find the trouble. Is he under financial pressure? Is his family life tense? Is he struggling for recognition? We should stop thinking of mental illness as a "germ" that grows inside an individual until it develops into a disease that demands hospitalization and medication to bring it under control. We will be more likely to understand the patient's illness if we investigate his environment and interpersonal relationships. Statistics show that one out of five of our military men in combat break down because of the high stress they are forced to live under. Now doctors are probing the high-stress situations of their civilian patients in the hope of stopping the high rise of emotional illness in civilians. When we understand that we are not fighting a "black magic germ" within a person, but circumstances in our power to change that are surrounding the individual, we see that it is foolish to fear and set apart the person who has broken while trying to fight his way through a high-stress situation.

Perhaps we need realistically to face these high-stress situations and ask ourselves if our attitude is adding to the tension of the patient. Many times a family thinks they are doing all that is expected of them when they assume the patient's financial debts. They often are saying to the world, "See what good guys we are; we're paying

for all of these bills and seeing that our loved one gets good care."
But they refuse to acknowledge the fact that they may be partially
to blame for his illness. These same people often let the patient
return to the house and keep reminding him that they are sane
and therefore always right, while he, the patient, has proved his
incompetence by breaking down and being hospitalized. It's not
always the guilty party who breaks, but the party who is the most
sensitive.

Because the person who breaks *is* often sensitive, he is less likely
to have the ability to fight his way back into a place of his own.
Not all patients can make it by themselves. These timid ones will
tentatively seek friendship and acceptance but, when rebuffed, will
retire and never regain the courage to try again. The social life
of these people depends on the public's acceptance and invitation.

One schoolteacher asked a psychiatrist, "One of my pupils has
been out of school getting psychiatric help. We all know where
he's been. Now that he is back, what can I do to help him and
what special way should I treat him?"

The psychiatrist said, "First of all, you are not his doctor nor
are you qualified to 'help' him. You wouldn't think of assuming
the post-operative care of one of your students who has had an
appendectomy, so do not try to practice therapy in the classroom.
As for special treatment, do you guard against the conversation of
or keep the children a safe distance away from a child just recovered
from the measles? Then treat this child just as normally. The children
will accept him back readily. Don't you as an adult set him apart
as a cripple."

This can be true in other places besides the classroom.

We can invite the patient to the neighborhood coffee. In everyday
conversation we can help her get over her reluctance to participate.

When the patient returns to his former interests, we can ask him
to serve on committees, offer him responsibilities, make him a part
of the group, so he doesn't feel as though he is an outsider being
tolerated by the rest of the members. He had capabilities that you
acknowledged and respected before his illness, so be ready to utilize
his talents again.

If the patient isn't ready to resume any duties, let him tell *you*
no. If he does refuse, respect his decision but leave the opportunity

open for further jobs by saying, "All right, but I'm going to keep you in mind for the nominating committee."

Remember, you may consider your silence to be consideration for the convalescent, but the patient is probably considering your silence as unconcern and rejection.

A small church had a member who broke down and was hospitalized. After she was released, she went back to the church and found silence and embarrassment from her friends. After a few weeks of this seeming rejection, she went home and, feeling she had no one to turn to, committed suicide. Sadly, a member of the church called and asked me to come to their church and speak to them. "We didn't know how to treat her and so we did nothing. We can't bring her back, but we want to be prepared if it ever happens in our church again. The woman was my sister."

In my own church I felt left out and ignored. A woman who was responsible for obtaining Sunday school teachers said to me one morning, "I've called every person on the membership list to teach the dialogue group and no one will say yes. At this point I would take just anyone."

I hadn't been called. I went home and thought about the course. It was one on learning to know yourself better. I knew from my experience in the last two years that I was qualified to teach the material. Eventually I volunteered. The committee thanked me and said they would call me.

I didn't hear anything further until two days before the class convened, when the lesson material was delivered to my home. I accepted the fact that I must have been the "just anyone."

The first day I taught, eight people attended. At the last session, three months later, there were thirty-five people in the room. I had proved to myself and to them that I could teach again. But I also remember that I was considered so incapable that I hadn't even received that every-member telephone call.

As a concerned person you should:

1. Watch for the patient's interest, his difficult situations, and his capabilities. If you see that he is having trouble rejoining his former groups, try to interest him in new organizations. Don't let him defeat himself by having to prove himself to people with closed minds, when he can cultivate new interests and friends.

2. Help him regulate environmental and interpersonal relationships that cause high stress.

3. Don't put him in a box. He will not be the same person he was before his illness. He has grown. His interests may be in a different area, his philosophy more serious. Give him room to grow. Don't free him from the locked doors of the psychiatric ward only to jail him in a cell walled up with limitations.

One morning, following a TV interview, an elderly man came up out of the audience to see me. As I went forward to speak to him, he said, "Please let me touch you." His trembling hands reached up and felt my arms and then lightly my face. "You had shock treatments?"

"Yes," I said.

"They are giving shock to my daughter-in-law, and I just wanted to see you up close to see if they had hurt you. I thought shock treatments were the last hope and she never was going to get well."

After a few minutes of reassurance that he should trust her doctor's ability, he shuffled away. As I watched, he raised his shirt sleeve and wiped away two tears.

I have noticed that many people want to touch me. As their fingertips stroke my features, I can sense an awakening in them. They see me as a person who admits to experiencing a breakdown and who now is capable of standing before people and speaking coherently. They especially want to see my smile and feel my responsive touch on their hand. My ability to function in a demanding situation helps them realize that their problem can also be conquered. I hope they remember and, when they too are well, pass on their knowledge to others who are fighting to come back.

11

The cry for help

One morning about 9:00 my phone rang. I answered it and a slurred voice said, "Help me."

I had been speaking to groups for almost six months and wasn't alarmed at receiving such a phone call from a stranger. Quickly I said, "Where are you and what have you taken?"

She managed to give me her address. I hung up, called Jim, and told him where I would be. "If I don't call back in an hour, come look for me."

I ran to the car and drove to the address. No one answered my knock so I found a side door open and let myself in. Lying on the couch was a woman I recognized from a talk I had given the week before. After that meeting she had come to me, crying, and I had talked to her for about an hour. Not quite strong enough to agree to an appointment with my doctor, she had at least agreed to my giving her his name on the back of my business card. Now she had cried help by taking a bottle of aspirins and then calling me before they could take effect.

I shook her until she would tell me her medical doctor's name. When I reached him on the telephone, he told me to induce vomiting. It was difficult for me to get the woman, who was quite heavy and already staggering, to the bathroom. I poured mustard and water into her, but though she retched, she couldn't bring up the medicine. She slumped to the floor, and I ran back to the phone to tell the

112

doctor I had failed. "Then you have five minutes to get her to emergency to have her stomach pumped," he advised.

I took time to call a FISH representative and quickly told her my problem. "There are two infants in the home and I can't leave until they have care," I explained.

Then I ran back to the woman. When I tried to make her stand, she cried, "Just let me alone. I want to die."

"Maybe you do," I said, "but you didn't take enough medicine to do the job. You're just going to be a mighty sick girl if you don't get yourself to the hospital."

When the FISH volunteer came, I drove the woman to the hospital and stayed in the waiting room until her husband arrived. He stammered out his version of their family troubles—frequent moves, lack of money, his wife's problem of overweight, two children too close together.

When at last her stomach was emptied, she was released. We drove back to her house. She was silent and ashamed of what she had done.

While we were gone, five other volunteers had come into the home and washed the dishes and thoroughly cleaned the house. The children were bathed, in clean clothes, and fed. In a few hours, several people had heeded this woman's cry for emergency help.

Now that the first step had been taken, her husband contacted a psychiatrist. After a preliminary consultation, the woman was admitted to the hospital. She responded to treatment and after three weeks was allowed a weekend at home. Another week and a half and she was dismissed.

The following evening one of the children began crying. The husband moved to the crib to pat the child. When the baby didn't stop crying, the pats became harder until he found himself beating it to stop the incessant sound of its crying. The next morning the husband was admitted to the hospital. By the time he was discharged, he had lost his job and the bills were staggering. His mother arrived on the next plane, helped them store their belongings, and with them started the drive back down south to their home town. In the last letter I received from the woman, she told me they were on welfare and both of them struggling to become competent enough to look for part-time jobs.

My heart aches for them in their long struggle. They had waited to go for help until their problems were almost insurmountable. And yet I have to wonder, how many times had they cried help but none of us heard?

Like most people, I was unaware of the effects of mental illness, its treatment or percentage of recovery, until it had happened to me. Up to that time I had occasionally heard whispers about people having been admitted to state asylums; I knew that shock treatment was supposedly a horror too terrible to mention and that people who broke with reality continued to be strange for the rest of their lives. But it had not happened to any member of my family close enough for me to get involved.

Simultaneously with my breakdown, several people I knew were admitted to the hospital—a friend of mine, one of my relatives, the daughter of one of my former neighbors and two other people from my church. This was enough to alarm me. I became concerned not only for my own health, but theirs. Already I wanted to know the whys and hows of temporary mental illness. In the hospital I started keeping notes for the day when I would be able to write of my experiences for my own therapy and for the comfort of others like me.

Many people had suggestions about how I should write my story. Some wanted an updated *Snake Pit*, others wanted a biting exposé of mental institutions, some wanted to be horrified. Very few, it seems, wanted to be enlightened. Finally I wrote a personal experience article, hoping it would at least speak to the other patients. I was not prepared for the reaction. Letters began arriving from all over the United States.

Many of them began as this woman did: "I just read your article and cried bitter tears. Why? Because I know what you have gone through and what lies ahead. I went through just such an ordeal."

Another woman wrote, "My friend called and told me to read your article; she said it was just like me."

Two elderly women wrote to express their love and sympathy. One enclosed a hand-carved sandalwood fan and the other a crocheted cross book mark.

One person wrote and assured me that if I ate soya powder and wheat germ I would be cured.

Thank-you-grams arrived from various businesses.

One letter was written on motel stationery. The woman was in the process of moving and while at the motel took time to confess her own breakdown.

An editor for a magazine where I published saw my byline and offered the magazine's appreciation for my telling a heartbreaking experience.

My sixth-grade teacher sent word that she was proud to have been one of my teachers.

Another wrote, "I had a nervous breakdown after the death of my little boy. Thank you for sharing your experience with the public. They will recognize your honesty."

"God has strange ways to paint the picture of life. With the gray the brightest colors do their best." This came from an elderly woman I had worked with in a restaurant ten years before. By cooking, cleaning, and sewing, she had supported her husband, who had Parkinson's disease, and her father, who had been bedridden since the early 1940s. She was well acquainted with the gray of life, but I had never known her not to smile.

I breathed a sigh of relief. I had been fearful of exposing my family to possible public ridicule. As I had no way of knowing how people would respond to reading of our experience, it was with relief that I opened and read each letter of appreciation.

Most of our letters were addressed only to Nancy Smith, North Canton, Ohio. The post office was in favor of returning them or dropping them into the dead-letter box. After persuading them to send a notice to all of their sorters they agreed to forward those they recognized in time. I was glad they did, because many of them included cries for help.

"I live in a small town and they are treating me like an oddity. Please talk to me."

"Ever since I have been ill I have been hoping that someone, somewhere, existed who knew and understood how I feel. I feel so helpless. Where do I start?"

"I was in a convent when I had my breakdown. I felt I had to stay there to prove myself. Truly it takes more than just an exterior faith to recover from a breakdown. A person has to regain faith in himself and overcome his guilty feelings. God made people to help other people. Faith helps, but it isn't enough. Why didn't someone recognize my complaints as nerves?"

"I would like to talk to you, but don't come when my husband is home. My father-in-law said it would be better to lose my mind and go to heaven than to go to the devil (psychiatrist) for help. Be thankful you have an understanding family. It is torture to be condemned for being what I am and basically they have made me what I am."

"I did all that the doctor said and now my wife turned against me. I realize that you are qualified by experience only, but I'm grabbing at straws. Should I give her a separation? I would appreciate your comments. Thank you for your article."

"From an active, busy woman who held a responsible, good-paying job, who had a great sense of humor and enjoyed life and people, I have become completely immobile. I'm afraid to be alone. Some days seem like an eternity. I re-read and re-read and re-read your article. One thing you said, 'Other people have fought what I am fighting and have recovered.' I have been trying only two years. Perhaps I will recover too."

How I wished I could give them something more in return than a friendly letter of understanding.

While the mail came in batches, the telephone never stopped ringing. The first three weeks I spent between five and six hours a day talking to strangers. I asked them not to tell me their names, because they talked to me of every possible personal problem and I didn't want to remember these confessions or be able to identify them with any particular person.

I soon learned that they could not be hurried. They had many things to talk about, and I was only expected to listen. Many of them began their conversation with "I know you can't help me but . . ."

One woman telephoned me from Florida and talked fifty-five minutes long distance. I tried to remind her of the bill she was running up but she was too intent on telling her story. Her husband had left her as soon as he discovered the diagnosis of her trouble. He was a lawyer and he was afraid the publicity would ruin his career. She had since been through two more marriages trying to find someone whom she could lean on. She had been a practicing psychologist at the time of her breakdown. She knew what was happening to her, but was helpless to stop it.

About half of the people who called were anticipating breakdowns. They read themselves into the article and were frightened when they knew they had these symptoms. They asked the procedure for obtaining help. I suggested a priest or minister, their medical doctor, a social worker, a clinical psychologist, a psychiatrist. One by one they would reject my suggestions, always with a shallow excuse. Eventually they would hang up, thanking me for my time and saying, "I'll keep trying a while longer; maybe I can make it without anyone knowing I'm having problems." I was disappointed when the telephone connection broke. I felt they wouldn't find success in that direction any more than I had.

Eventually Jim noticed my exhaustion. I was beginning to dread the ring of the telephone. I was so tired of being asked for help that I couldn't give. Each person needed time and love and I couldn't be the savior for all of them. I felt defeated as we closed the house and left for two weeks vacation.

As I lay on the sand by the ocean, I thought of all the faceless people I had touched in the last few weeks. Sharing my experience wasn't enough; they wanted someone to help them through their own trial. But how?

When I came home I prepared four speeches. One on my breakdown and recovery, one on treatment and psychoanalysis, one on mental illness and the family, and one on faith and hope. If I couldn't help each patient, then their families and friends would have to be educated on how to help them.

I began talking one night a week to people, mostly secular groups. The churches still seemed reluctant to say, "We, too, need instruction."

I told program chairmen, "I will not come just to entertain you or to shock you, and I hope you will not interpret my talk as a plea for pity. I realize that doctors often use technical terms and talk over the heads of the audience. They forget how little we really know about mental illness. I will try to inform your group in laymen's language what they can do to help individuals or themselves if need be. After the talk there will be time for questions. They may ask me any question they want to. Nothing will embarrass me. If I cannot answer or prefer not to answer, I will tell them."

The speech soon proved to be the shortest part of the evening. My longest question and answer period was two and a half hours. At the end of that time I pleaded with them to stop, because I was too tired to think any more. During the refreshments my coffee gets cold as I try to answer questions that are too personal to be asked from the floor. The last question is always at my car, because even as I leave a cluster of people follows me.

I can't believe that I am that accomplished a speaker. I have to believe that the public is hungry for knowledge in this field. If this is true, then it is a much needed awakening.

I arrive home late and very tired, but content. I have to force myself to sleep quickly. The next morning I know the phone will ring and I will need to talk further to someone from the evening before. The calls come in early, because this is the hardest time of the day for a mental patient. He sees the day stretched before him and he can't believe he will have the strength to live through it.

I'm willing to talk to these people, but they have to realize one very important thing: when I say, in my talk, that people must give love, understanding, and compassion to patients, I'm not saying that I'm going to be that person for every patient.

When I suggest to a woman that she talk to her husband the way she is talking to me, she says, "It wouldn't do any good, he wouldn't listen."

"Then you must make him listen. I won't be around for you to lean on."

Sometimes a representative of a family will call and plead with me to come and talk to a member of the family. Though it is often difficult, I have to say, "No, *you* talk to that person. You give him the love you want me to give him. You hold his hand. It will be you, not me, who will live with him the next years. It's your responsibility." Just reading about mental illness or listening to a lecture isn't enough. The people have to practice the advice they receive.

Jim has teased me and suggested that I might like to open a commune for patients in our backyard. Yes, at times I would like to collect these bewildered and lonely people and keep them close, but that is unrealistic. The time of collecting mental patients in institutions is past. Now probably one-half of the people requiring psychiatric care receive it in psychiatric wards in hospitals rather than in institutions. Since 1957, more people are being discharged than are being admitted. And, as more families are able to communicate as families, the time of hospitalization will be shortened and the rate of discharge increased.

One afternoon I picked up a woman at the mental health day-care center. I was on FISH call and she needed transportation home. She was a tall woman, red-haired, loud-spoken. After she had crawled into the car and we had started, she said, "You'd better be scared. I'm a mental patient."

"I know."

"Well, aren't you scared I'll hurt you?"

"I'm a mental patient too. Are you afraid I'll hurt you?"

She looked at me through a haze of cigarette smoke. "But I was in the hospital."

I smiled, "So was I."

We were like two children trying to outdo each other.

"I had shock treatments," she said.

"So did I."

"I had seven."

"I had fourteen," I replied.

She looked at me a few minutes and then she grinned. "You win, you were sicker. Now let's talk."

And we did talk, warmly and deeply, the rest of the ride to her home.

Occasionally I will run into one of the people I was with in the hospital, and we have an emotional reunion there on the street. It is wonderful to see a person neatly dressed, walking briskly with his or her family, smiling and competent, when I have only known that person during his depression. The change is miraculous.

The first time it happened to me I was waiting to pay my check in a restaurant, when I recognized the woman in front of me. I touched her arm. "Do you remember me?" I asked.

She frowned and said, "Yes, from the hospital. You were one of my nurses, weren't you?"

"No, honey," I laughed, "I was there right along with you."

And much to the surprise of the other patrons we burst into tears and embraced.

She is now working and is no longer under a doctor's care.

Sally, my roommate, and I saw each other another evening and she came to visit me. She proceeded with her third divorce, has moved to an apartment and is working. This time she isn't running to a new man but is learning to find security in her own judgment.

Little Kim is now a young lady of seventeen. Her parents and she have moved to another state. Kim says the house is beautiful, situated in the country up in the hills. She is now attending public school, and though she still needs a doctor's help, she hasn't run away again.

Carrie, our grandmother, was the only one who was institutionalized—not because she would do harm to herself or to others but because she had no family and there was no other place for her to go. I hope she's content and that when she asks, "Any whiskey, cigarettes, or a chew for Carrie?" someone occasionally can comply.

Many people have seen and are seeing the gray of life, but the colors do begin to show again.

Depression does burn out . . . happiness does return.

12

Love, compassion, and understanding

There is still little known about the human mind, and there can be no formula for recovery. No one layman, or doctor, can assure any family of an absolute cure, a guaranteed treatment, or even a time line to health. Each person is an individual, with different environment, problems, access to professional help, will to recover, and acceptance by his family and associates. The story I have told you is not the only way. It is *one* way that brought positive results.

As I look back I can see that I had every advantage.

1. I had a doctor who was competent and patient and who took a personal interest in each of his patients.

2. I had a family who stood by me at the time of crisis and gave me love during the years that followed. They were not "goody-goody" martyrs who utilized my illness as an opportunity to receive pity from the public, but people who attempted to react to situations with a healthy attitude.

3. Though we were not wealthy, we did have the finances to enable me to have the proper hospital care and therapy. Some of this was possible through hospitalization, some through the patience of the doctor to wait for payment, and some through a gift that paid the last $1,000 to remove the financial worry from Jim.

4. I had the will to recover. When the time came in my recovery to take up the fight for my own soul, mind, and body, I fought! If mental health was maturity and growth, then I would mature

121

and grow. If psychotherapy helped a person to know himself better, then I would work hard and learn to know this complicated person of Nancy Smith. If wallowing in self-pity meant possible reoccurence of illness and hospitalization, then I wouldn't cry, whimper, or complain.

In the book *Minds That Came Back** I read of people who had been more seriously ill than I, and who had gotten better. I wouldn't be content to be an invalid; I would get well. I refused to be intimidated when tempers flared between Jim and me, or when I wasn't accepted into a group. I silently swore to them, "I'll get well in spite of you. No one will return me to depression."

An elderly man recently told me, "I saw you clench your fist, and I thought to myself, when that girl clenches her little fists no one or nothing can stop her."

A short time ago I was clenching my fists in withdrawal and depression. Now I clench them with determination.

I can't foretell the future. I never know when circumstances I couldn't tolerate could develop so that I would withdraw from reality again. But I'm not going to anticipate calamity and worry. Instead I'm using what I've learned about myself to practice preventive medicine for my mind.

An unknown writer has said, "A person's character is marked not so much by what life does to him as to the reaction he makes to life's circumstances."

We all get knocked down in life. And perhaps one of our stumbling blocks is a mental breakdown. We can either bewail our fate or we can take up our life and make of it what it could be under the circumstances.

These past few years have been many things to me.
1. Hell
2. Discouragement
3. Struggle
4. Progress
5. Accomplishments
6. Success
7. A hard-worked-for miracle
8. Opportunity

---

*Walter C. Alvarez, *Minds That Came Back* (Philadelphia: Lippincott, 1961).

Writing this book and reliving those years have been both pain and joy for me. It has forced me to look closely at myself and other people and at circumstances. It has made me sort out my life until I could see a pattern running through it. It has let me see events in retrospect so that I no longer have to blame anyone, even myself, for problems or disappointments. It has caused me to search inside myself to put into words my philosophy and feelings of faith and God. Perhaps I haven't done it very well. Maybe as you read this book you saw shreds of my illness and still see a person groping for understanding.

More than a year ago a woman asked me if I was normal again. I didn't know how to answer her. At various times since then I've asked myself that same question and have been tempted to say, "Yes, I've made it. I'm well." But each time I'm reluctant. And each time when I go on, a look back at the intervening months makes me realize that I'm still changing and progressing.

At one time my prayer was, "Just let me be calm." I couldn't even imagine ever feeling happy. I would never be lighthearted again; that was too much to ask. Yet now the majority of my time is happy and peaceful. I do have plans and ambitions. I've decided life is worth living after all, if only to receive a spontaneous hug from Tammy after she finishes a successful ride on her two-wheeler.

I pray that as I have written and you have read, we have both found strength and knowledge and faith. I've written in the hope that you will never have to write, "No one comes here but me, and so the way is dark and unexplored." Others have walked this path, and each of us, as he recovers, needs to share what he has learned to help those coming after. Each of us has to remember the illogical feelings, the times of indecision, fear, and guilt, so we can say, "I understand."

As the young girl in the convent said, "God made people to help other people." When words fail, we can open our arms or clasp a hand. We all possess the intangible tools of love, understanding, compassion, and faith.

I can think of no better closing than Malcolm Boyd's "Prayer of Discipleship":

"Send me."

But where, Lord? To do what?

To bring pardon where there has been injury in a life I casually brush against at my daily work? . . .

To help turn doubt into faith in a person with whom I live intimately in my circle of family or friends? . . .

To bring joy into a life, consumed by sadness, which touches the hem of my life at a drinking fountain? . . .

"Send me." Send me next door, into the next room, to speak somehow to a human heart beating alongside mine. Send me to bear a note of dignity into a subhuman, hopeless situation. Send me to show forth joy in a moment and a place where there is otherwise no joy but only the will to die.

Send me to reflect your light in the darkness of futility, mere existence, and the horror of casual human cruelty. But give me your light, too, Lord, in my own darkness and need. Amen.*

For in this prayer lies the beginning.

---

* From *Are You Running with Me, Jesus?* by Malcolm Boyd. Copyright ©
1965 by Malcolm Boyd. Reprinted by permission of Holt, Rinehart and Winston, Inc.